THE BLIND DOCTOR
THE JACOB BOLOTIN STORY

A Biography

ROSALIND PERLMAN

BPB
Blue Point Books

THE BLIND DOCTOR: The Jacob Bolotin Story.
Copyright ©2007 Rosalind Perman and Blue Point Books

Publisher's Cataloging-in-Publication
(Provided by Quality Books, Inc.)

Perlman, Rosalind.
    Jacob Bolotin : the life of a blind doctor / by Rosalind Perlman.
    p. cm.
    LCCN 2007927821
    ISBN-13: 978-1-883423-13-1
    ISBN-10: 1-883423-13-9

    1. Bolotin, Jacob, 1888-1924. 2. Physicians with disabilities—United States—Biography. 3. Blind—United States—Biography. I. Title.

R154.B72P47 2007   610'.92
                    QBI07-600134

Edited by Cathy Feldman
Cover & Book Design by Cathy Feldman
Book Production by Blue Point Books

First Edition
10 9 8 7 6 5 4 3 2 1

Published by Blue Point Books
P.O. Box 91347
Santa Barbara, CA 93190-1347
800-858-1058
bpbooks@west.net • www.bluepointbooks.com

ACKNOWLEDGEMENTS

All publishers dream of having an amazing book dropped into their hands. *The Blind Doctor: The Jacob Bolotin Story* is just such a book. Jacob Bolotin was remarkable in every way, not only for his own accomplishments but also as a passionate and powerful spokesman for a "fair deal for the handicapped." Rosalind and Alfred Perlman recognized how special he was and devoted the last part of their lives to creating this book. Ultimately Rosalind turned to the Santa Barbara Foundation to create a trust that would make sure *The Blind Doctor* was published and to create a national award in his honor. Even though they were unable to see this final product, we think that they would be very pleased.

Many people contributed to the publication of this book, and we would like to thank them for their efforts. The Santa Barbara Foundation staff, including Raynette Cornejo, Suzanne Farwell, Tanya Gonzales, Chuck Slosser and Laura Wyles, has done a terrific job of supplying materials, information and support to pave the way for the publication of *The Blind Doctor.*

Others who graciously provided materials and assistance include Stephen Marshall, nephew of Rosalind Perlman; Nancy Martz, a friend of Rosalind Perlman; Richard Weldon, Attorney; Brock L. Bigsby, Assistant Scout Executive, Chicago Area Council Boy Scouts of America; Jea Nae Wood, Executive Director, Illinois-Eastern Iowa District of Kiwanis International, and Karen Yakovac, Director of Marketing, Kiwanis International.

At the National Federation of the Blind, we would like to thank Dr. Marc Maurer, President; John Paré, Director of Public Relations, as well as Kristina Wadia and Chris Danielsen.

Special thanks to Sara Miller McCune for her "sage" advice, as well as to my friends Laurie Leighty, Arlene Stepputat, and Barbara Tzur for carefully reading the manuscript and offering valuable suggestions and corrections.

– Cathy Feldman,
Editor & Publisher

INTRODUCTION

As a child growing up in Chicago, Rosalind Perlman had heard of "the blind doctor," Dr. Jacob Bolotin, who was well-known and greatly admired by people in his native city and around the world.

When she met her husband, Alfred Perlman, she learned that Dr. Bolotin's wife, Helen, was Alfred's aunt. Alfred and his widowed mother had lived with the Bolotins for four years until Dr. Bolotin's tragic death at the age of 36 in 1924.

While Alfred was in the Army during World War II, Rosalind wrote and produced a weekly radio series for the Chicago Tribune station, WGN, and taught script writing. After Alfred returned from serving overseas, the couple moved to Santa Maria, California, where Alfred taught high school.

In Santa Maria, Rosalind taught speech and drama at Hancock College for the Pacific Conservatory for the Performing Arts, where she frequently starred in productions. She also wrote a regular column for the Santa Maria Times.

Rosalind and Alfred always dreamed of writing a book about Dr. Bolotin to share the story of this amazing man who had devoted the last third of his short life to changing society's perception of what a blind person could do. Based on Alfred's vivid memories and those of his Aunt Helen, other friends and family members, as well as media clippings, photos and other documents, Rosalind wrote many drafts of the book before her husband died in 2001.

After Alfred's death, she devoted the rest of her life to making sure the book was completed. *The Blind Doctor: The Jacob Bolotin Story* is the result.

The Blind Doctor is the vibrant story of a truly great man who was described in the words of his contemporaries:

It is one of the most amazing instances of mind triumphant over physical handicaps that the world has ever known... [Dr. Bolotin] will rank with Helen Keller as one of the wonderful blind persons of history.

Philadelphia Inquirer 1914

To insure that Dr. Jacob Bolotin would continue to inspire others, after her death in 2004, Rosalind left a bequest in the name of the Alfred and Rosalind Perlman Trust to the Santa Barbara Foundation to publish *The Blind Doctor* and to establish an annual award: the Dr. Jacob Bolotin Award for the Blind. This national award will be presented to blind people or organizations that have made a significant impact within the blind community beginning in 2008. The Foundation is working with the National Federation of the Blind to administer the award.

PROLOGUE

Excitement flowed about the room in great surging waves as the students awaited their renowned professor. It was the first session of the 1920 school year, and the huge lecture hall at the Chicago College of Medicine and Surgery was filled to capacity. Suddenly, the room fell silent as the door opened and a man in his early thirties of medium height, black hair topping a round boyish face, walked briskly to the podium, a mahogany cane moving lightly before him. He turned and faced the class.

"Good morning, gentlemen. I am Dr. Jacob Bolotin." He moved his head slowly from side to side as he spoke, and his intense gaze seemed to focus upon every student.

An audible gasp swept the room. There were no dark glasses, no hesitant, shambling walk, no traditional vacant stare. His eyes looked completely normal. Yet the students knew that this man, one of the great heart and lung specialists in the United States, had been born totally blind.

Turning from the lectern, he walked to the blackboard, slid his fingers along the rail until he found a piece of chalk, picked it up and printed in large letters:

BOLOTIN

"Gentlemen," he said facing the class, "many people pronounce this `Bo-LOW-tin.' In my family, we pronounce it `Bo-LA-tin.' But you'll probably be calling me many names before the year is over." He grinned happily as laughter swept the hall. "Now, gentlemen," he said, as the merriment subsided, "let's talk medicine."

For two hours he lectured on diseases of the chest, holding the students' attention with ease. Many noted that he used no teaching aids, neither books nor notes. As he concluded, they applauded vigorously and several rushed forward to identify themselves as students in his course on diagnosis the previous year.

A few, reluctant to leave, gathered in small groups to discuss their new professor. Three young men standing in the aisle regarded him skeptically. Erasing the board, Bolotin's keen ears caught the whispered conference and he smiled to himself. It was the conversation that followed every year's opening lecture.

"Do you think he's really blind?" one asked, "I mean, really?"

"Well," a second said," he's supposed to be, but I swear he looked directly at me three times!"

"Me too, right at me," the third agreed. "He can see as well as I can! That cane has to be window dressing."

"Okay, okay," the first broke in, "but did you notice, he never once referred to notes, not once for two hours? Only prof I've ever had do that! He's gotta be blind."

"But how could he write on the board if he didn't have some sight?" the second argued.

Grabbing up his books, the first hissed, "I'm gonna ask him."

"No, no don't! He might not..."

But the student had already accosted Bolotin at the door. "Doctor," he said, "please, sir..."

"You have a question?" Bolotin asked, turning to face the student.

"Yes sir, I do! Are you, I mean, are you really...," he stopped, red-faced.

Bolotin smiled patiently. It was the usual question. "You want to know if I am really blind."

"Y-y-yes sir," the student stammered.

"Well, I have no eyesight." Bolotin replied. "I was born blind, but my other senses serve as my eyes, so I feel no handicap."

"But, sir," the student persisted, "how could you become a doctor?"

Bolotin laughed, "It's a long story. Let's just say it wasn't easy!"

THE BLIND DOCTOR
THE JACOB BOLOTIN STORY

CHAPTER 1

On January 3, 1888, his mother's piercing scream was the first sound the infant heard as he emerged into his dark world.

The midwife was pleased. The birth had been smooth and unusually fast, as though the little one could not wait to be born. Suspending him by his heels, she gently slapped his small buttocks until his indignant wails filled the room. She wrapped him in a warm swaddling blanket and laid him in his mother's arms.

"Mazel tov, Faga," she announced cheerfully, "here is your number seven! A fine, healthy boy."

Faga lay motionless, her arms rigid. Then her hand moved slowly to fold back the bit of blanket that shielded the baby's face.

Standing beside the bed, Louis saw her hand hesitate and move back from the blanket. Quickly, he dropped to his knees and brushed a damp curl from her forehead. "Faga, my love, it's a boy, a beautiful boy!"

There was no response. Faga lay tense, unmoving, staring at her husband. He saw the dark fear in her eyes, her face taut with dread.

He leaned forward to catch the whispered words, "His eyes.... His eyes..."

"He sees, Faga, he sees. Our little Jacob has eyes that see."

Still, she did not move.

"Look at him, Faga! Look at him! He's a perfect boy!"

Slowly, Faga lifted the blanket. Two huge, shining brown eyes gazed back at her.

With a great cry, she cuddled the little one, her face radiant.

"Tonight," Louis said as he caressed the baby's cheek, "I go to the synagogue and give thanks to God for such a blessing." Faga nodded and their tears of joy fell upon the tiny bundle lying between them.

The midwife stood silently. She had understood Faga's terror. Her last two babies, Sarah and Fred, had been born blind. Unwilling to disturb the joy that enveloped them, she tiptoed quietly from the room. It would be years before she could describe, without tears, the sweetness of the scene she had witnessed.

Jacob was a happy baby. Where two-year-old Fred, born blind, was often petulant and fretful, Jacob glowed with life. His parents noticed he loved sounds and brought him rattles and tiny bells. He would reach for the toys, shake them beside his ears and gurgle with delight. His brothers and sisters sang to him and cuddled him. Four-year-old Sarah, also born blind, was ecstatic when the baby clung to her finger.

Yet, as the months passed, Faga felt a growing uneasiness. "Louis, why Jake doesn't look at us when we talk to him? Something's wrong with the baby."

"Faga, stop imagining things."

"I'm not imagining!" Worry etched her face and voice. "He turns ears to us, not eyes!"

Louis laughed, "Of course he turns ears, because ears hear, not eyes."

She was not comforted. "No, Louis, no! He's like Sarah, like Fred, exactly like Fred."

"Faga, don't be foolish. He acts like Fred, because he mimics. Babies always mimic."

Her fears subsided. Louis was right. When Jacob gradually began turning his head toward anyone entering the room and looking directly at her as she nursed him or spoke to him, her heart sang. She scolded herself for so foolishly doubting God's blessing. He had, indeed, given them a perfect son and she prayed constantly for forgiveness.

Louis teased her about her silly misgivings and they laughed, together, at the baby's charming antics. "You know, Faga, I think he's going to be a great orchestra conductor," Louis often declared as they watched the tiny hands wave happily about whenever Henry, their oldest son, practiced his violin. A song would immediately stop the baby's crying and calm his upsets. Above all, he loved Faga's lullabies and would settle contentedly in his crib until he fell asleep.

Not until Jacob began to crawl did Faga's submerged fears resurface. Yet she could not doubt God and remained silent until the baby, crawling rapidly across the floor, banged his head into a chair. She grabbed him up and rocked him to stop his crying, but she knew. It was Fred all over again. Fear, like a corroding acid, seeped into her heart.

She waited until the evening meal was over and the children bedded down before she confronted Louis. "Why does Jake bump into everything when he crawls? Sarah and Fred, they bump into everything too..." Her voice quivered on the brink of hysteria. "Our other babies crawled around everything. Sadie's baby next door crawls around everything."

"Faga, please," Louis pleaded.

"No, if Jacob has eyes that see, why he bumps into everything?"

"He's a baby, Faga. That's how babies learn."

"No!" Faga screamed at her husband. "He's blind. Jacob is blind like his sister is blind, like his brother is blind." An uncontrollable trembling wracked her small body. "God forgive me. Another blind baby I bring into the world."

Louis held her close and stroked her hair. "Fagela, stop tormenting yourself. Jake is normal."

"Louis, I must know," she whispered, her body tensed and rigid, "please, I must know!"

Without a word, he picked up a jumping jack from a small pile of toys. Motioning Faga to silence, they approached the crib. The baby lay cooing quietly, staring at the ceiling. Slowly, Louis leaned forward and held the toy before the baby's face. He pulled the strings and the little clown, in his gaudy, polka-dotted suit, began somersaulting again and again. Faga's eyes were riveted upon the baby's face, searching for a movement, a flicker, a sign of awareness. Louis swung the jumping jack from side to side then in wider and wider arcs. Jacob did not move. His eyes stared motionless at the ceiling, his soft cooing undisturbed.

From deep within her, Faga screamed. Frightened, the baby began to wail. With a wild sob, Faga snatched up her baby and began rocking him in her arms as the tears flowed unhindered and unceasing.

"We still don't know!" Louis said tensely, his face drawn, his lips white. "I'm going for the doctor."

Faga sat frozen, pressing the little one to her protectively in the warmth of her love.

When the doctor saw her stricken face, he smiled cheerfully. "Stop worrying, Mrs. Bolotin. It's probably just some simple upset."

Faga placed the baby in his crib and the doctor began his examination.

Louis slipped his arm around his wife and together they waited. Time hung suspended, a soundless void in which only the doctor existed.

At last he straightened and turned to face them. The Bolotins stood mute. They knew, yet they waited.

The doctor's words came slowly. "Your son," he said, "cannot see. There is no hope he will ever see. Jacob was born blind."

CHAPTER 2

Hurrying to the streetcar stop a block away, Louis shivered as the wind clutched him in its icy blast. He tightened his shabby coat about him, straining for every ounce of warmth. The snow lay in wet, slimy puddles of black slush that oozed through his shoes and sent chills up his legs. He was steeped in guilt. Since they had arrived from Poland six years ago, he had been unable to provide Faga with enough money to feed the family. She never complained. Somehow she always managed to put food on the table for the children. She was a marvel. It was her constant sewing and mending and patching of clothes handed down from child to child that kept them looking clean and neat. Soon his two oldest sons, thank God, would be old enough to get jobs. And now—two blind sons. What would become of them? How would they support themselves? Worry clung to him like a shroud.

He was going to be late for work. Luckily, his boss was a patient man. He understood. Louis vowed to work harder and make it up to him.

He walked rapidly, head down, hugging the building to shield himself from the wind. Sprinting around the corner, he slammed head-on into a man standing there. A sharp whoosh of breath burst from the man's mouth as he fell heavily to the sidewalk. Furious with himself, Louis rushed to aid him. "I'm sorry," he mumbled, then defensively, "but you ought to look where you're going."

The man was apologetic. "I would if I could, mister. I would if I could." Helping him to his feet, Louis stifled an involuntary gasp as he saw the crudely lettered cardboard sign hanging by a cord around the man's neck.

I AM BLIND

7

The man wiped the slush from his face with a patched coat sleeve and then began groping around the wet sidewalk. Louis saw the pencils, the tin cup and the scattered coins lying in the blackened snow. Quickly, he gathered them up and returned them to the blind man.

"I'm sorry," he said, numbly, engulfed in shame. "I'm sorry, my fault, I should look where I'm going."

"It's okay, Mister, no harm done."

"I think I found all your money."

Louis paused to still the ache inside him. "How old are you?" he blurted out.

"Thirty-two," the man replied.

Almighty God! Would his sons be standing on street corners with tin cups and pencils when they were thirty-two?

Louis felt a sudden surge of hatred for all the blind man represented. "Why you can't find a better way to earn a living?" he demanded, bitterly. "Why do you have to be a beggar?"

The man lowered his head. "It isn't what I want to be," he replied wearily. "It's all the world will let me be." He lifted his head and spoke so softly Louis strained to hear the words above the clatter of the approaching streetcar. "Nobody gives a damn about blind people. We're just useless cripples. Nobody gives a damn, Mister."

"I do!" Louis said savagely. He reached into his pocket, grabbed a handful of coins, flung them into the cup and fled to lose himself in the crush of people boarding the already over-crowded streetcar.

He waited until Faga was lying beside him in their ancient bed that creaked with every move before relating the incident. As she listened, he felt her body grow rigid.

When his tale trailed away into silence, Faga spoke slowly, her voice was hard and cold. "To our sons, this will never happen." She raised herself on an elbow and bent low over her husband's face. "Louis, promise me, promise before God, to our sons, this will not happen. Promise me!"

"I promise, Fagela. Somehow, with God's help, our blind children will never be beggars." He placed his arms around her and held her close. Kissing her, he felt her cheeks wet with tears. "Please, Fagela, no tears. God knows our troubles. He will help us."

"No, God will not help. With blind babies he punished us! For our sins, God punished us. What sins did our babies commit? Why does God punish our babies? Why?" Her tears were knives in Louis's heart.

"Please, Fagela, tears don't help."

"No, nothing will help. Only eyes that see." She pressed herself against him needing the comfort of his love.

He caressed her gently until slowly the tears subsided. "God is just," he murmured softly. "He has reasons for everything. Who knows, someday, maybe we understand."

He rocked her until she fell asleep. But he lay awake, the blind beggar's words like some diabolical refrain beating inside his brain:

Nobody gives a damn...
Nobody gives a damn...

CHAPTER 3

Jacob was a precocious child, quick, alert, intelligent. Faga soon learned he was also a child who refused to accept failure.

"Louis, remember when Fred began to crawl he bumps into things? He hurt himself, so right away he stops crawling? Jake doesn't stop. He crawls fast, so fast he bumps hard and hurts himself. He's all-over black and blue. When he bumps, he cries, but again he crawls. Nothing stops him."

Jacob questioned everything. In a world bounded only by what he could hear and feel, it was not enough to learn the feel of a glass. He had to know why a glass felt different than a cup, why his nightgown felt different than his shirt, why some things were round and others square. While a sighted child would ask why the sky is blue and birds fly, he had no concept of sky or color or the flight of a bird or what a bird looked like. Louis brought him a toy bird that chirped when he squeezed it. Jacob was ecstatic. He hugged and kissed the toy and took it to bed with him. At last he knew the source of the sweet singing that thrilled him when Faga took the children to the park.

Jacob's passionate love of animals began shortly after his cousin Harry Bolotin opened a livery stable next door. One day, strange sounds coming from the bedroom window awoke the child from his nap. Curiosity quickly overcame fright. He walked slowly towards the sound, his arms outstretched. Suddenly, his hands encountered a terrifying object. It moved! It snorted! It was like nothing he had ever known – smooth…yet rough, soft…yet hard, warm and moist and long. Even the smell was different. It yielded a new, wondrously enchanting sensation.

His ecstatic shrieks brought Faga running into the room. Her first instinct was alarm as she saw the toddler caressing one of Harry's horses that had poked his head through the open bedroom window. Then she saw how gently the horse nuzzled the child's cheek and her blind son's rapture. Silently, she went back to the kitchen and returned with several cubes of sugar.

"Mama, Mama," the child cried, "what is this?"

"Is a horsie, Jake, the head of a big horsie. Here," she lifted the boy from the floor and guided his tiny hands along the horse's muzzle, "Here's his mouth; here's his nose. How does it feel?"

"Wet...funny...and big."

"And here, way up are his eyes."

"Is he blind, like me?"

"No, no! He's looking right at you. He likes you."

"I like him, too, Mama." Impulsively, the child leaned forward and kissed the horse. "I love Horsie! Can I take him in the house to play with?"

"No, my darling," Faga laughed, "He's big! Too big. He has four long legs and a tail bigger than you. Here are lumps of sugar for him. He will like them. Hold out your hand." She pressed the sugar cubes into Jacob's hand and guided it toward the horse's mouth. The child giggled and squealed as he felt the horse gently scoop up the sugar from his hand.

From that morning on the horse came every day for his sugar treat. The horse and the boy became fast friends. Later, cousin Harry took Jacob into the stable where the astounded child discovered the size and shape of the body that was attached to the head.

Faga taught her blind sons the alphabet, how to spell their names and how to count. When a lesson was finished, Jacob begged for "more lesson." His curiosity was endless.

"If I say no more candy," Faga told Louis, "he is fine, but when I say no more lesson, he cries. For him, enough is never enough. And never he forgets. Fred I must tell many times till he remembers. Jake I tell once only."

When adults, unable to answer Jacob's barrage of questions, tossed them aside with stumbling generalizations, his disappointment was not lost on Louis. After several months, he had saved enough to buy a second-hand set of encyclopedias. These, he hoped, would provide the information needed to satisfy the child's curiosity.

When Fred turned six, it was time to enroll him in the public school attended by all his siblings. The day before classes began, to save carfare, Faga walked the mile-and-a-half to the school and filled out the enrollment card. Leaving the office, she suddenly turned back and asked, "Is it possible, please, to talk to the principal?"

"There's no need, Mrs. Bolotin," the clerk replied. "If Fred is anything like your other children, he'll do fine."

"Maybe," Faga persisted, "he should know my Fred is blind."

"Oh! Please wait. I'll call him right away."

The principal was apologetic. "I'm sorry, Mrs. Bolotin. At this school, we cannot accept blind students. We have to follow the rules, you know. I'm sure you understand."

Faga didn't understand. She was furious. Louis accepted the verdict. "Maybe it is better. Tomorrow we take Fred to Professor Bamberger at the Jewish school."

Jacob had understood that he was too young to go to the school his older brothers and sisters attended. But if Fred was going to a different school, so was he. He sang, he bubbled. He apologized to Horsie explaining carefully that he wouldn't be there to feed him his daily sugar treat because "I am going to school!"

"Louis," Faga pleaded, "tell him. Tell him he can't go."

"No," Louis replied, "we wait. Maybe Jewish school rules are different from public school rules. Besides," he added impishly, "what can Bamberger say? Is either no—or maybe—yes."

Faga dressed the boys in their holiday suits and the little family, father, mother and two sons, presented themselves to Gabriel Bamberger, principal of the Jewish Training School. "We are Mr. and Mrs. Bolotin. We've come to enroll our sons, Fred and Jacob."

"Good," Bamberger, tall, with a trim beard and mustache, a skullcap perched atop a mop of curly black hair, beamed at them. "They look like fine boys." He turned to Fred, "How old are you, young man?"

"Six," Fred replied.

"Excellent." Bamberger patted Fred's shoulder. "The perfect age to start school."

"I'm four," Jacob announced and held up four fingers to prove it. "I'm perfect age too."

Taken aback, Bamberger glanced quickly at the parents. He saw their tense, worried faces. "I wish," he said gently, "we could take them both, but we cannot accept children under six."

"Please, please understand," Louis said respectfully, "the children have always been together."

Professor Bamberger adjusted his glasses and cleared his throat. "Mr. Bolotin, I understand how you feel. Believe me, I understand, but it is against the rules of the school. Fred we will be happy to accept. As for Jacob, he will have to wait until he is six. I'm sure you understand. We can't break our rules."

"No," Louis said firmly, "only God's rules are holy and can't be broken. But, you will please excuse me, Professor, school's rules are man's rules, not holy, and sometimes is good to break them."

Bamberger was puzzled. "Why can't your Jacob wait?"

"Because," Louis explained, "they never been separated. They need each other. Both are blind."

For a long moment the principal stared at the anxious parents. "I see your problem," he said with sudden huskiness. "I understand. But, I think you should know, we've never had blind students here and have no facilities for..."

"They good boys," Faga interrupted. "They never give trouble."

"No, I'm sure they won't." Bamberger smiled, "Well, rules can often be broken. Let me talk to Jacob."

Seating the tiny child beside him, the professor asked in the syrupy voice adults reserve for small children, "Jacob, tell me, why do you want to come to school?"

"Because, I want to learn like my brother."

"But your brother is two years older than you. He is ready for school. You are still too young."

"I know as much as he does. Why does it matter if he's older than me?"

Bamberger was enchanted. Above all, he loved intelligence. He smiled happily at the Bolotins. Then, turning back to the boy, he spoke as man to man.

"The work is hard, Jacob. Do you think you can keep up with the other children?"

"I know my ABC's and I can count, too."

"You know your ABC's? Can you recite them for me?"

His voice high with excitement, Jacob raced through the alphabet without stopping for breath.

"That's very good, Jacob, and you say you can count, too? How far can you count?"

"To a hundred! Clear to a hundred! Can the other children do that?"

"Well, some can and some can't, because they are just beginning."

"But I already know how. Please let me come to school. I will study hard, I promise. I will be very good. I won't ever bother anybody. Please let me come."

Bamberger could restrain himself no longer. He lifted the boy from his seat and held him close in his arms. "Jacob," he said, "four years old is almost as old as six. I think you are ready to start school."

CHAPTER 4

Every weekday morning, Faga took the children to school, gave them their boxes of lunch, kissed them and watched them grope their way slowly down the long corridor. She waited until they had safely disappeared into their classroom.

Then, as always, she returned home through a maze of tears as envy stabbed at her heart to see the other boys, the sighted boys, run freely unhampered past her little ones. Several times she saw older boys deliberately block the children's way or tease them by snatching their hats or their lunches. Fred would begin to cry, but Jacob, bursting with indignation, would fight back. He would lash about banging into other children, doors and walls while loudly demanding the return of their property. An avenging Faga, her heart pounding with fury, would rush to protect her little ones and retrieve their belongings.

When she related the incidents to Louis, he refused to sympathize. "This is hard world," he said. "Our boys must learn to take care of themselves."

But Faga could not rest. She went to see Professor Bamberger.

"Mrs. Bolotin," he said, "the boys are just playing. They will never hurt your children. But I will put a stop to it. That I promise you."

The next day, Bamberger called a special assembly and asked Faga to be there. She sat quietly in the rear of the hall as Bamberger said, "Boys, I am going to tell you a story. One day, many centuries ago, when the great Rabbi Hillel lived, a Christian challenged him to sum up the teachings of our Bible while standing on one foot. Hillel immediately lifted one foot and said, 'Do unto others as you would have them do unto you.' That, boys, is the heart and substance of our Torah. It is the

Golden Rule. That means we must treat others with kindness, especially those less fortunate than we are. Think if you were deaf or blind or crippled, would you want others to tease you or bully you or torment you? Remember the Golden Rule. Carry it in your minds, your hearts and your souls every day of your lives."

The teasing stopped abruptly. From that day on, the older students became protective of the young brothers. Faga's worries ended. Not until years later, when she related the story to Jacob, did Louis learn of the little episode.

Jacob loved school. He learned quickly. His teachers smiled and called him a sponge, always ready to absorb more.

After a few months, Professor Bamberger realized it was imperative for the boys to receive specialized training for the blind, training his school could not offer. He went to see the Bolotins.

Honored by a visit from the revered head of the school, Louis ushered the Professor into their tiny parlor and seated him on their only upholstered chair while Faga brought tea and noodle pudding. They waited politely for him to speak.

"I have come," he told them as he stirred sugar into his glass of tea, "to talk to you about your sons."

"They cause trouble?" Faga burst out anxiously.

"No, not at all, Mrs. Bolotin. You have two splendid boys. They're bright and eager to learn. But," he paused, hesitantly; "there is a problem."

"A problem?" Louis murmured worriedly.

"Yes. Their teachers are deeply concerned. You see, they don't know how to... that is ... they're not trained to help handicapped children, especially blind children."

Louis was dumbfounded. "They can talk to them, explain to them..."

"Talk is not enough, Mr. Bolotin. Jacob and Fred can't read books. They can't see pictures the teacher draws or see what he writes on the blackboard. They can't make things with their hands like other children or even play at recess like other children."

"Play is not important," Faga said, stonily, "only learning is important."

"Exactly, Mrs. Bolotin. But at our school your children cannot learn. But there is a fine school, a school for the blind, where your children will learn. The teachers there are specially trained to work with the blind."

"How far is this school? Can we walk there?"

Bamberger hesitated. This was the hurdle he had dreaded. He braced himself for the battle.

"No, Mrs. Bolotin, you cannot walk there. The school is in a town called Jacksonville."

"Not here in Chicago?" Faga was incredulous.

"No, but Jacksonville isn't far from Chicago."

"You are telling us to send our children away from their home?" The terror in her face sent chills through Bamberger.

"You must, Mrs. Bolotin."

Faga stared at him, aghast. "They are babies! Who sends babies away from their mama and papa?"

"Excuse me, Mrs. Bolotin," the Professor forced himself to face her agitation, "your children are not like other children. They must learn how to walk on the street, how to take care of themselves in a world that can be cruel to the blind. They must learn Braille. "

"What is Braille?" Louis asked.

"It's the way blind people learn to read and write."

Louis sat transfixed. "You are saying my sons will be able to read, to write?"

"Yes!" Sensing an ally, the Professor turned eagerly to Louis. "At the Illinois State School for the Blind they will learn to read and write as well as anybody else. They will get the education they need to make something of themselves."

Louis looked at his wife. Her face wore the look of a tigress defending her cubs.

"Faga," Louis said, hesitantly, "maybe it is best for our children. Maybe we should..."

"Louis!" her fury was raw and deep. "What you saying?"

"I'm saying, Faga, you asked me to promise..."

"But not yet, not yet! Louis, our Jacob is not even five years old!"

"But, Faga..." Louis pleaded. "If is best for our children... Think, Faga, think! If they can learn to read, to write, maybe we should..."

"No!" Faga shrieked. "They are babies! We will talk when they are older! Now no one takes away my babies from me!"

For Faga, the subject was closed. But Louis, haunted by the Professor's plea, conferred secretly with Bamberger. Together, the two conspirators hatched a plot. As the plot took shape, Louis brought the professor a brown paper bundle of clothing he had smuggled out of the house.

Throughout his lifetime, Jacob loved to amuse his audiences with the harrowing tale of "THE DAY MY BROTHER AND I WERE KIDNAPPED!"

In early January, one week after Jacob's fifth birthday, Faga brought the children to school, admonished them to "be good" and kissed them goodbye. As she disappeared around the corner, Bamberger immediately dispatched an older student to bring the brothers to his office.

Leading them down the hallway, the student whispered, "What did you do?"

"I don't know." Fred whispered.

"We didn't do anything!" Jacob asserted, indignantly.

"Well, you must have done something," the student replied.

Jacob felt his heart pounding. "Will we be punished?"

"I guess so," the student admitted sadly. "Anyway, good luck." He knocked on the office door and fled.

Bamberger threw the door open with a cheerful, "Come in, boys! Come in!"

Clinging tightly to each other's hand, the two moved slowly forward, their heads bowed low in helpless acceptance of the guilt that was undoubtedly theirs.

"Children," Bamberger said, "I have a surprise for you."

"Is that our punishment?" Jacob asked, softly.

"Punishment?"

"For being bad?"

"Bad!" the Professor chuckled. "You've never been bad. Why would I punish two good boys like you? No, it's not punishment. It's a wonderful surprise. Today you're going for a ride on the train."

Jacob was instantly curious. "What's a train?"

"You'll find out," the Professor teased.

"Are the other boys coming, too?"

"No, this surprise is just for you and Fred."

Jacob sensed a new adventure and was aglow with excitement, but Fred was hesitant. "Are Mama and Papa coming with us?" he asked.

"No, not today. Keep your coats and hats on and take your lunches. I already have on my coat and hat, and here is my lunch." He rattled a large paper bag, "Inside is another surprise for you."

Fred was not impressed. "I'm not going!" he declared flatly. His lips tightened. "And Jake isn't either."

"Yes, I am!"

"Boys, please!" Bamberger knelt beside Fred. "Do you want Jake to go by himself?" he asked gently. "You're the big brother, Freddie. He needs you to take care of him. So, now, will you let him go alone?"

The child's lips trembled. "No," he whispered.

"Then you must come, too. Besides, if you don't go you'll never find out what all my surprises are, and you want to know, don't you?"

Fred nodded, his reluctance still intact.

"Good!" Bamberger rose to his feet, "We must hurry to the depot or we'll miss the train."

Jacob's sightless eyes widened. "What's a depot?"

"Jacob, do you want to stay here and ask questions, or do you want to go?"

"Go! Go! I want to go!"

"All right, then, let's move."

Bamberger picked up Jacob, took Fred by the hand and led them to the horse-drawn cab waiting at the curb. The driver clicked his tongue, snapped the reins and the cab rolled smartly down the street.

Jacob was enthralled. "I love the train," he shouted, "I love the train."

The driver, the father of one of Bamberger's students, chuckled as the ever-patient Professor explained, "This isn't a train, Jacob. This is a cab. Soon you will learn what a train is!"

At first, the hissing, steaming, roaring, clanking monster terrified the boys. Confused, disoriented, they sat silently on the seat next to Bamberger, two small huddled bundles of misery. Even Bamberger's teasing, "What's the matter, Jacob, no more questions?" failed to calm them. He decided it was time for his first surprise.

"Boys," he said, "hold out your hands. I have something for you." He placed a large, flaky cream puff in each outstretched palm. The boys were fascinated. Faga's baking had never introduced them to anything like it.

"What is it?" Jacob giggled.

"Smell it. How does it smell?"

"Ummm, nice, sweet."

"How does it feel?"

The boys conferred, "Kind of crispy and there is something soft at one end. Can we eat it?" Jacob sensed something extraordinarily delicious.

"Well, why don't you try?" Bamberger was elated. The children's curiosity had vanquished their fear.

As they gobbled down the pastries with delight, Jacob began to sort out the intriguing sounds that surrounded him. The rhythmic clickity-clack of the train wheels, the plaintive tooting of the whistle, the clanging of the bells and the chug-chug-chugging of its engine. These were new, wondrous, strangely satisfying sounds. The swaying sudden lurches, grinding stops and starts all yielded enthralling unknown sensations. The mixture of voices and laughter, the awareness of people moving up and down the aisle provided a lure Jacob could not resist. When Fred refused to budge from his safe haven beside the Professor, Jacob went off on a voyage of discovery. Groping with outstretched arms, clinging to the backs and arms of seats, he moved slowly down the aisle filled with pride and exhilaration at making his way alone.

His fellow passengers were annoyed. With every jolt of the train, this rude, mannerless child fell against people in their seats and bumped into those trying to move past him. It annoyed them even more, that instead of apologizing, he laughed and giggled.

Then, with frightening suddenness, Jacob's first brave venture into independence became violent. As the train leaned into a long curve, a series of sharp lurches sent him hurtling into a tall, pudgy boy about eight or nine playing in the aisle.

"You pushed me," the boy shrieked.

"I didn't mean to," Jacob replied as he untangled himself.

"You did too! You did it on purpose!"

"No, I said I didn't mean to. Honest!" Alarmed, Jacob tried to break away from the belligerent voice. "I didn't even know you were there."

"That's a big fat lie!" The boy gave Jacob a shove that knocked him to the floor. "I was standing right smack in front of you."

Uncomprehending, terrified, the five-year-old struggled to his feet, fighting back his panic. "But I can't see you," he explained, his voice trembling.

"That's another fat lie. You were looking right straight at me." The bully stepped hard on Jacob's foot and the little boy gasped with pain. "You're a coward. That's what you are, a big, fat coward!"

"I am not!"

"You are, too." His tormentor burst into a taunting singsong. "Coward! Coward! A big, fat coward!"

"I am not a coward! You take that back."

"Who's gonna make me—you?" the boy snickered.

A fist caught Jacob hard just below his chest. With a moan he doubled forward, his arms clutching his stomach, as a wave of pain flooded his body. Another blow sent him crashing to the floor. From a vast distance, he heard the mocking, "Who's gonna make me?"

"I am," he cried. With clenched fists, he lunged towards the hateful, taunting voice. He met only empty air.

"Come on! Make me! I dare you."

Turning around, Jacob lashed out again and again, searching for the elusive voice that came from nowhere, yet everywhere. Suddenly, with a mocking laugh, the boy caught Jacob's arms, pinned them down and began kneeing him in his chest and stomach. The pain was terrifying, but Jacob refused to cry out. "Give me a nickel," hissed the bully, "and I'll stop."

"I don't have a nickel," Jacob gasped, "and even in did, I wouldn't give it to you." With a desperate effort, he wrenched himself free and began flailing wildly about, searching for the disembodied voice he could neither see nor find. From the empty air came a vicious rain of blows so fierce he couldn't breath. Excruciating pain and panic dissolved his bravado into helpless sobs. "Stop it," he screamed, "stop hurting me! Please stop hurting me!"

At the far end of the coach, above the clatter of the wheels, Bamberger heard Jacob's cries. Within seconds, he held the hysterical child in his arms.

"It's all right," he murmured.

"He kept hitting me," the little boy sobbed.

"He bumped into me hard! On purpose!" The victorious assailant flung the words at Bamberger.

Fighting to control his anger, the Professor looked down at the preening child. "My son," he said, "you should be ashamed of yourself! Jacob is only five years old. He's half your size. If he bumped into you, it was because he didn't see you. This little boy is blind."

From the coach ahead, the boy's father came looking for his missing son. When the child saw his father, he whooped with joy and quickly wrapped himself around his father's legs.

The boys nodded numbly. He held them in a long embrace, kissed them, and stumbled away. Not until he had gone did the children let the tears flow as a stranger took them by the hand and led them into a strange and frightening new world.

That night, the two children cried themselves to sleep.

Early the next morning, Jacob awoke and reached out automatically for Fred. His hand found only a terrifying void. Startled, he called softly, "Fred? Fred?" There was no answer. Suddenly, he remembered. The train—the bully—Professor Bamberger. They weren't home; they were in a school. But where was Fred?

He slid out of bed and groped with his hands around the edge till he came to the foot of the bed. Reaching out, he took a few tentative steps. There was another bed. That's where Fred would be. Gently, he ran his hands over Fred's face. Jerked awake by the feeling something was crawling over his face, the boy sleeping there, Michael, began screaming hysterically and flailing his arms wildly. One arm hit Jacob hard in the nose, and it began to bleed. Bewildered, frightened, hurting, Jacob fell to the floor. By now the other boys in the dormitory had awakened and joined in the screaming.

The bedlam brought the matron, Katie Halpin, in breathless alarm. Her glance swept the room. One bed was empty.

"It's all right, children," she soothed as she searched for the missing child. "Everything's all right. Nothing to be afraid of."

Gradually the din subsided, but Michael wasn't finished. "Something crawled across my face!" He shrieked. "I hit it! I hit it hard!"

"It was just me," Jacob sobbed from the floor.

There he was—the missing child. Relieved, Miss Katie picked Jacob up, sat him on his bed and quickly placed a large handkerchief under his nose to stanch the flow of blood.

"I didn't mean to hurt him. Honest I didn't." Jacob was trembling. It felt good when Miss Katie put her arm around him and helped him hold the handkerchief till the bleeding stopped.

"There," she said, wiping away the mingled blood and tears. "That feels better now, doesn't it?" She waited until Jacob's trembling stopped, then asked gently, "Tell me, Jacob, why did you get out of bed?"

"I was just looking for my brother. I thought that was him right beside me. I just want my brother," he pleaded.

Miss Katie turned to Michael. "Did he hurt you?"

Michael was honest. "No," he admitted slowly. "But I was awful scared."

"Yes, of course you were. We'd all be scared of something crawling over our face. But Jacob didn't mean to. He thought you were his brother. They were always together at home. Wouldn't it be nice to let them be together here? What do you think, Michael?"

"No!" the answer was firm. "This is my bed, and I don't want to change it."

"Then we won't change it. We'll just swing your bed around with Fred's. Is that all right with you, Michael?"

"Well," Michael was reluctant, "I guess, as long as I keep my own bed, it's okay."

"Good. That's very nice of you. I know you and Jacob are going to be great friends."

The beds were reversed, and from that time on the brothers were always together.

The school lived up to its long, impressive name. Its goals were clear and simple: teach students how to face the daily hazards and problems of the blind philosophically and without complaint.

When Jacob hurt himself by bumping hard into a staircase and complained to the teacher, she said simply, "Jacob, the stairs were here first, and you'll just have to remember that." He also learned stairs were made to walk on, not fall down on.

Here they would learn to become self-reliant, independent, productive citizens. They would receive the specialized training that would enable them to compete in the world of sight.

To this end, the students were not pampered, pitied or babied. They were expected to be obedient, complete their assignments, obey the rules of the school and adhere to its strict code of moral and social conduct. But they would be loved. The teachers were carefully chosen for gentleness, patience, compassion and love for children. It was that love that enabled Jacob and Fred to gradually overcome their grief and the sudden crushing shock of being separated from their family.

It began that first morning when Miss Katie placed them in the line of boys standing before the large double doors to the dining hall. In a moment, a loud bell rang and the boys filed in quietly to their tables. Miss Katie led Jacob and Fred to a table with six other boys. When they tried to sit down she whispered, "No. Not yet." Another bell rang and the students all recited grace. That finished, the bell rang again—the noisy scraping of chairs told the boys they could now sit down. Soon, they heard the clanking of dishes as breakfast was served. The bowl of cereal was different than Faga's but tasted pretty good. Then a plate of hot food was placed before them. It had a strange smell.

"What is this?" Jacob whispered to Fred.

"I don't know." Fred was as puzzled as he was.

Jacob was intrigued. "It smells good."

Miss Katie laughed. "It is good. Here, I'll slice it up for you. It's hot ham and eggs."

Fred gasped. "Oh! We can't eat that!"

Miss Katie stopped slicing. "Why not?"

"Because," Fred stammered, "the Rabbi said it's traif."

"Traif?" Miss Katie was curious. "What does 'traif' mean?"

Suddenly, Fred was tongue-tied. Jacob came to the rescue. "It means," he struggled with the word, "it means…unclean."

"Unclean!" Miss Katie's tinkling laughter rang across the hall.

The boys at their table began snickering.

"Unclean!" Miss Katie shook her head. "Tell me, do you think we'd give you anything unclean? We all eat the same food, all of us. Do you think we'd want to eat anything unclean?"

She saw the children's humiliation and Jacob's hand grope for Fred's.

Quickly, she placed a hand on each boy's shoulder and said softly so only the two could hear, "It's not the same as home is it? But will you do something for me? Just for me?" There was no response.

She cut two small pieces of ham, placed one on each boy's fork and put the forks into their hands.

"Here," she said, "try it just for me. If you don't like it, we will never serve it to you again, I promise."

Curiosity overcame Jacob's hesitation. He ate the bit of ham and blurted out in stunned surprise, "It's good. It's really good. I like it."

But Fred sat with clenched teeth.

"It's good, Fred. Try it, you'll like it, too."

Reluctantly, slowly, Fred nibbled the ham. "It doesn't taste dirty," he admitted. "I guess it's okay."

Miss Katie was elated. "Good," she said. "Now eat and enjoy your breakfast. Then you'll be ready to start school."

Neither Louis nor Faga ever learned that their sons were eating and enjoying the forbidden food, pork, for the nine years they attended the school.

The boys were enrolled in the kindergarten, which was the equivalent of public school grades 1 and 2. They began developing their sense of touch, of "seeing" with their fingertips. During a single month the boys examined a snake, beetle, grasshopper, lobster, duck, caterpillar, butterfly, rat, cocoon and cat. They discovered the difference between tomato seeds and cucumber seeds, between a walnut, a peanut and a grape.

Jacob reveled in the rich variety of shapes, sizes, textures and construction. He refused to let go of any object until he had examined every detail.

To develop dexterity of hand movement, they were taught beadwork and basket making. They wove mats, modeled in clay and began the study of Braille.

Even as a young boy Jacob realized knowledge would be his greatest ally in the sighted world. Along with knowledge, he would develop a memory so keenly sharpened that nothing heard or experienced would be forgotten. As they progressed through the upper grades and through high school, he waged a ceaseless battle for knowledge, memory and self-discipline while studying the usual subjects — English, Math, Geography, History and Science.

Jacob thrived on challenges and the intricate Braille system of raised dots was one that demanded intense coordination of hand and brain. It fascinated him, but he found it almost too easy. He challenged himself to sensitize his fingertips until he could read through a handkerchief, then another handkerchief and another until he could read easily through sixteen layers of handkerchiefs.

When he quietly revealed this ability to some fellow students, they hooted in derision. "Impossible!" they declared. Jacob refused to back down. Soon the teachers were drawn into the fray. Finally, it was decided he would be put to the test in front of the student body. The teachers would write a page in Braille, and Jacob would have to read it after the Chapel service Sunday morning.

Fred was worried. "Can you really do it?"

Jacob laughed. "It's easy. Of course I can do it. I wouldn't say if I couldn't. Stop worrying. You'll see."

Sunday morning services were no sooner over than a murmur of anticipation flowed around the hall. Jacob sensed the excitement. It was the kind of challenge that he loved. He was ready.

"All right everybody," Mr. McKay, principal of the boys' high school called out. "Let's all be quiet and let Jake read this page the teachers have prepared. Will you please come up to the platform, Jake?"

Grinning happily, Jacob was already on the way. He handed Mr. McKay the sixteen handkerchiefs. "Please count them, sir." His words had the clarity of a bell.

Suppressed giggles erupted as Mr. McKay waved each handkerchief aloft and began counting, "One, two…" Soon the students joined in the counting, "… fifteen, sixteen!" The principal took the prepared paper out of his pocket, placed it on the lectern and announced, "I have placed the sixteen handkerchiefs over the paper. You may begin reading aloud please, Jake, whenever you are ready." He was as certain as the audience that the feat was impossible, but he hoped for Jacob's sake that he would not make a fool of himself.

Jacob placed his fingertips on the paper and began reading it easily and clearly. When he finished there was a dead silence. Mr. McKay stood up.

"Absolutely perfect!" His words reflected his amazement.

Jacob didn't want the ovation that followed. This was simply a task he had given himself, and he was satisfied that he had achieved it. He had no way of knowing that years later his uncanny sensitivity of touch would astound the entire medical world.

By the time he graduated, he had read every book in the school's Braille library.

The sense of hearing for the blind is as essential as breathing. Sound is to the blind what light and color are to the seeing.

Instinctively, Jacob began training himself to listen, to distinguish the endless variety of sounds that surrounded him. Gradually he was able to identify people not only by their voices but also by the sound of their footsteps.

One day, when Minnie Coley, his typewriting teacher, walked by him in the hallway, he said politely, "Good morning, Miss Coley."

She took a few more steps, stopped and turned back. "Jake," she asked, "how did you know it was me? I didn't say a word."

Now Jacob was puzzled. It had been so natural. "By your walk," he replied.

"Oh! Is my walk funny or something?"

Jacob was mortified. Obviously she felt insulted. "No, no Miss Coley," he hastened to assure her, "you have a nice walk. It's just... Well, you see, everyone's walk is different, so when I hear it, I know who it is."

He admired Miss Coley. She was a teacher who brooked no nonsense. She expected her students to learn to type their one-page "papers" with accuracy and speed. She demanded "perfect papers." An error in spelling, punctuation, capitalization, a mistake in spacing, hyphenation or the striking of one letter over another ruled the paper out of the "perfect" class. This required intense concentration and coordination. To Jacob it was just another challenge that had to be conquered, and he became an expert typist.

To train the ear, music was also heavily stressed. Students were taught piano, orchestra and band instruments or singing.

Though Jacob and Fred loved music, and Jacob had learned to play several band instruments by ear, neither had any musical talent. An item from the school's bicentennial report dated 1894-1903 states:

"Jake Bolotin, 1898 piano student. Without ability. Moderate progress, poor memory. Slow mentally. In first year much good progress."

Another entry in the report stated:

"Fred Bolotin, 1898 Piano. Has had several trials and has inflicted more upon his teachers. Dismissed."

From the time he was a toddler, Jacob identified the people around him as well as inanimate objects by odor. It was an ability that came as naturally to him as learning to walk. Here at Jacksonville, he challenged himself to memorize the odor of every student and teacher, as well as hundreds of inanimate objects whose odors were nonexistent to the sighted. He never forgot an odor, as he never forgot a voice, a name or the touch of a hand. Eventually he recognized over two thousand patients by odor. It always amused Jacob that this ability, which came so automatically, was a constant source of amazement to the sighted world.

Throughout their lives, Jacob and Fred credited the physical training classes at the school for rescuing them from the timid, hesitant, shambling walk so typical of the blind. Daily exercises and drills in the gym taught them to stand erect with head up, to walk with courage and confidence, unaided and unaccompanied.

The boys lost count of their many falls chasing balls that had bells inside them or their crashes on the baseball diamond. The falls hurt, but the glorious exhilaration of running freely was a joy they had never known. The painful black and blue bruises that covered their bodies were badges of progress as they gained strength, self-reliance and independence.

Manual training required the use of tools to develop hand dexterity. The boys made fly nets, hammocks and brooms. They constructed wooden objects using saws. planes, knives, hammers, awls and rasps.

"This made excellent instruments out of my hands," Jacob related in a magazine article in 1919. "Without them I could not do anything. My work requires very sensitive hands."

It was the school practice to have a student from each classroom give a speech or recitation during morning chapel exercises. The student had to find his way to the platform unaided and speak before the entire student assembly. Each room had its day, and Jacob was frequently called upon to represent his class.

It was invaluable training for a man who would later be asked to give as many as four or five speeches a day in a vast variety of hospitals, universities, schools and organizations, and occupy the Chair of Diagnosis at three universities.

The students led busy lives and little time was left for play, but the years passed quickly. Suddenly graduation was only a week away.

A full year before the boy's graduation, Faga and Louis had begun saving for the trip to Jacksonville. It would be the first time they had seen their sons since Professor Bamberger had them taken to the school. Now, dressed in their finest holiday clothes, they sat hand-in-hand in the crowded auditorium watching their young sons walk down the aisle. In a shimmering haze of pride and love, they saw their Jacob, the Valedictorian of his class, erect and confident, climb the stairs to the stage, walk unaided to the podium and face the audience to deliver his address.

"The first day I came here," he told the assembled parents and faculty as he concluded his speech, "I walked into a wall. When I cried, the teacher said to me, 'The wall is there and you must learn to live with it.' The sighted world is out there and we blind graduates must learn to live in it. We are not afraid. We are blind, but we are not stupid. We have as much to offer the world as sighted graduates, and we promise you, our parents and our teachers, that we will achieve success and make you proud of us."

Jacob in 1903

As the applause surrounded them and parents began hunting for their children, Louis and Faga stood, confused and alone, in a corner of the auditorium. Miss Katie led the boys to them. Suddenly two handsome young men were shouting, "Mama! Papa! Mama! Papa!" Long arms were wrapped around

Louis and Faga, and they were smothered with hugs and kisses and tears of joy. Soon they were all crying as they clung to each other, unwilling to let go of the joy that engulfed all of them.

Louis murmured a prayer thanking God for giving them the strength to endure the nine torturous years of separation. It had been their sacrifice to give their boys the education they needed. Faga gazed in awe at these beautiful young men and knew it had been worth it.

Now her two blind sons were ready to face the world.

CHAPTER 6

At the turn of the century, the nation was exploding into the Industrial Revolution. Chicago, the exuberant city stretching across Lake Michigan's southern shore, was an inexhaustible source of new ideas, new factories, mills and foundries, new industries and technologies. She needed workers with the vitality to match her volcanic energy. Jobs were plentiful for men, women and children with whole healthy bodies, sharp eyes, nimble, capable hands and minds that could be quickly trained in the skills needed to run the city's commerce and industry.

But not all who applied were hired. The blind, the deaf, the crippled were human refuse unneeded and unwanted. In 1903, society had neither time nor inclination to concern itself with their needs. There were institutions and asylums for the disabled. They were seldom seen on the streets. It was understood that these unfortunates would never marry or have families of their own. If, sadly, a blind man found it necessary to support himself, he could always beg or sell pencils on busy street corners.

But jobs in the cold, practical, unsympathetic world were only for the "normal" in full possession of all their faculties. Jacob refused to accept this verdict. Obsessed with his desire to assist his impoverished parents, he was determined to find a job.

When family friends warned him he was living in a wishful dream, he would laugh and reply, "Only people who dare to dream accomplish anything in this world." He would assure them he was no longer a child. He was fourteen. He was a man. "I can't be a burden to my parents," he would explain earnestly. "I must earn my own way and help Papa support our family. I've had a fine education and there are many things I can do and do well. I know it. Just give me time. I'll find a job."

Fred was more fortunate. Cousin Harry hired him to take charge of feeding and cleaning his horses.

"But," Cousin Harry apologized to Jacob, "I can't afford to hire both of you. Maybe later. I'm sorry."

Jacob wasn't discouraged. Fred's success convinced him that, somewhere in this great city, there was a job waiting for him.

Each evening, after their meager supper, Louis unfolded the newspaper and read the want ads aloud. With his Braille stylus, Jacob made a listing of the jobs he believed he could fill. Early the next day, he set out on his rounds, traveling from place to place to apply for the position. The employer's response never varied. "We do not hire blind people."

Yet he persisted, often walking miles between locations to save the few cents carfare. He was keenly aware of the sacrifice Louis was making to supply him with carfare, money that should have been used for food. He promised he would repay it all with interest once he got a job. With characteristic optimism, he was certain he would eventually find one employer willing to give him the chance he needed.

None did. After months of fruitless search, he was forced to admit failure. "I couldn't even get a job shoveling snow off a back porch."

There was one dividend. The job search required him to travel unaided throughout the busy city and gave him the confidence and independence that later enabled him to travel alone throughout the United States. He soon became a familiar figure to streetcar conductors who painstakingly called aloud every street whenever he was aboard.

One blustery, freezing morning in late February, shortly after his fifteenth birthday, Jacob answered a knock at the back door. A woman stood there carrying a large basket filled with boxes of kitchen matches. Faga noticed the woman's threadbare coat, her face pinched with cold under a heavy babushka, her shoulders hunched against the wind.

The woman smiled at Faga. "Would you buy some matches, madam?" Her hand shook as she offered a box for inspection. "Two hundred matches for only four cents."

"Of course," Faga replied. "Matches I always need. You save me trip to the store. But you are shivering. Come inside. My kitchen is warm. So, now," Faga grasped the woman's arm and led her to the stove, "sit by the stove, warm yourself and have glass of good, hot tea."

When the steaming liquid was placed before the woman, she wrapped her frozen hands around the hot glass. "Oh," she breathed, "this feels good."

Jacob knew a fresh box of matches that Louis had brought home yesterday was sitting in the cupboard. But he also knew his mother could never turn anyone away. He went to the jar of change that Faga kept on a shelf, sorted through the coins and brought the woman four pennies.

As her body warmed, Faga's genuine concern warmed the woman's heart and she soon found herself recounting her months of failure to get a job. Jacob listened, fascinated. Here was a healthy, sighted woman unable to find work because she was over forty. "Too old," employers said. Even the man from whom she obtained her basket of matches doubted her ability to long endure the physical punishment involved.

Jacob was torn with curiosity. " May I hold your basket for a minute," he asked.

"Of course," she smiled at the eager boy.

Jacob lifted the basket and swung it back and forth. "It isn't heavy. It isn't heavy at all."

"No, it isn't heavy in the morning," she said wryly, "but it keeps getting heavier all day long. Thank you for the tea. I feel much better, now. Bless you, madam, for being so kind to me. I don't often meet people like you. But I must get back to my matches." She rose, took the basket from Jacob and walked to the door.

Jacob rushed after her. "Please, may I ask you a question?" Curious, she turned back. "Can you earn very much money selling matches?"

She was amused by Jacob's obvious embarrassment. "Well, it's different everyday," she replied, "because it depends on the number of hours I put in. But I make enough to support myself and my children." She paused and then added, "Why do you ask?"

"I can't find a job because I am blind." Jacob heard her soft gasp of compassion. "Could I sell matches?"

The woman studied the boy standing tensely, waiting for her answer. She didn't want to discourage him, yet the truth had to be told. "It depends on you," she said gently. "Can you get around the city by yourself?"

"Yes, yes I can. I've done it many times. I have a whole map of the city in my head."

Still, she hesitated. Finally, she spoke carefully, "You will have to find your way in and out of buildings, climb endless stairs. Sometimes they are broken or blocked or covered with ice or snow, like today. And there are dogs and children..." Her voice trailed off into silence, but her hesitation was lost on Jacob. He was aflame with excitement. He was young. He was strong. Stairs didn't frighten him. He had learned how to manage stairs. At last he had found a way to help his family. He would sell matches.

CHAPTER 7

The next morning, icicles dripped from the windows and February's raw, freezing wind roared down from the Arctic. It was barely past dawn when Jacob awoke.

Faga, wrapped in her old bathrobe, was standing beside his bed. "Jake," she spoke softly to avoid awakening Fred, "Not today. The wind is bad. It will be hard for you to walk."

"No, Mama, I want to go today."

"Too cold. Maybe tomorrow, Jake."

"I must get my basket today so tomorrow I can start selling."

"Jake, please. The weather is much too bad outside."

"Don't worry, Mama. I'll wear a sweater under my coat"

At 7:00 AM, Chicago's dilapidated wholesale district was already functioning at its usual frenzy when the streetcar conductor guided Jacob to the sidewalk. "This is a bad place," he said. "Be careful."

Jacob was puzzled. Why would a match shop be a bad place? A passerby assured him he was at the address the match lady had given him. He took a few tentative steps forward and felt himself walking down a steep slope. Horses and wagons thundered past him. Men yelled at him, "Get the hell outta the way!" He stood paralyzed with fright. What horror had he stumbled into? The match shop would be safe. He had to find the match shop.

Slowly, he searched ahead with his cane, then snatched it back quickly as a wagon nearly ran over it. He held it tightly to his chest shaking with a terror so intense he could hardly breathe. Never in his young life had he experienced such nerve-shattering din.

He could not see the cavernous old warehouse whose gigantic, open loading docks protruded like giant fangs. But his keen ears caught the frenzied coming and going of endless lines of clattering horse-drawn wagons, vans and carts driven by cursing, shouting men. He felt himself drowning in chaos as his dark world dissolved into a wild pandemonium of screeching wheels and clanking carts, rattling wagons and horses thundering by in front of him and in back of him so closely that he could feel the rush of wind as they passed. Voices piled upon voices came from everywhere, furiously shouting, "Get the hell outta here! Move your goddamned ass!"

His senses screamed that he was in mortal danger. He wanted to run, but where? Confused, panic-stricken, he stood helpless in a world he could neither see nor understand.

Suddenly, rushing to the loading dock, a wagon driver caught sight of a boy standing directly in his path. He yanked in the reins with such force that his snorting horse reared up on his hind legs. "Goddamned idiot!" he shrieked, "I nearly killed ya! Move, damn ya, move!"

Jacob longed, desperately to move. But, which way, where?

"Get the hell outta my way!" the driver raged.

Jacob stood motionless, held in a vice of terror.

"Move, you bastard! Move!"

"Where?" the frantic boy screamed. "I can't see! I can't see!"

Within seconds, two strong hands lifted him bodily and carried him away from the tumult. He sensed he was inside a large building. The din had receded. The fearful rush of activity around him had lessened. The hands set him down on something hard.

"It's all right, young fella. You're safe here." The man's voice was quiet, compassionate. He sat down beside Jacob and waited until the boy's trembling subsided. "Feeling better?" he asked. Jacob nodded. "Good. Now tell me, what the devil are you doing here?"

"I came for matches," Jacob mumbled, "a basket of matches."

"Matches!" the workman laughed uproariously. "You nearly got killed for a basket of matches? Why?"

Jacob's head dropped low. "Because nobody will hire me," he whispered. "I'm blind." The laughter stopped, abruptly. "At least," Jacob explained, "I can sell matches."

The man was silent for a moment. Then his arm tightened around the boy's shoulder. "Come on," he said, "let's go to the match shop. It's just around the corner on the other side of the building. Hold on to my arm. I'll take you there."

"I don't understand. This is the address that the match lady gave me. What did I do wrong?"

"It's the right address, all right, but this building is two blocks square. You just got off the streetcar a block too soon and came to the loading docks, the last place on earth for you to be."

He led Jacob through a bewildering succession of rooms and doorways until, at last, he felt the sidewalk under foot.

"This is it, Heiner's Match Shop." The man gently placed Jacob's hand on the doorknob.

Impulsively, Jacob turned and hugged the man. "Thank you. Without you, I don't know how... " He fumbled for words. "I mean, I could never have..."

The workman enveloped him in a tight, warm hug. "It's okay, son. I've got a boy your age. I hope if he is ever in danger, someone will be there to help him. Just remember," he said as he released Jacob, "get off at the next stop and you'll be right in front of this door. Good luck with your matches, son." He shook the boy's hand and was gone.

Jacob slowly pushed the heavy door open. A freezing blast of wind came in with him.

"Close the door!" a voice with a thick German accent bellowed. "You want I should die from the stinkin' cold?" Kurt Heiner, a hundred pounds overweight, lifted his bulk from the chair, slammed the door and returned to his desk. "So, kid," he yelled, "talk. I'm busy man."

Thoroughly cowed, Jacob began to stutter.

"God in Heaven!" Heiner sputtered, "talk English. What you want?"

"Matches," Jacob mumbled, "a basket of matches."

"Aha! The kid talks English and wants a basket of matches. Good. So, how many baskets? How many matches?"

"Just one basket."

"Okay. Stacked over there by the wall. Take what you want."

"I can't. I'm blind."

"My God, the kid's blind. Goddamned, sonofabitch, why you wasting my time? Go home, kid."

"I won't go home till I get a basket of matches." Jacob was astonished at his own audacity.

"Kid, you crazy, you know that? Tell me," the heavy voice softened a bit, "you ever sell before anything?"

"No, sir."

"It ain't easy, beggin' on street corners. It ain't fun."

"I'm not a beggar," Jacob replied indignantly. "I won't stand on street corners. I'll do like the match lady who came to our home. She was selling door-to-door. I'll do that, too."

"Aaaach! Another nut," Heiner moaned. "Nuts and perverts. Nuts and perverts and crazy blind kids! I'm sick of all of you. But, what the hell, money's money." He emitted a long worried sigh. "They buy my matches I don't give a damn they deaf, dumb, blind and wear monkey suits." Another sigh. "Okay kid, pay four bucks and you got your basket matches."

Jacob gasped. "Four dollars? I haven't got four dollars."

"So, how much you got?"

"Carfare. I only have carfare."

Heiner spat out his disgust. "Looney kid. Go home! You want matches? Come tomorrow with money."

Jacob knew the basket was lost, but still he argued. "There's no place I can get that much money."

"So! How you buy matches?" Heiner shouted angrily, "with air?"

"No, sir," Jacob replied, quietly, "I thought first you sell and then you pay."

"First you sell, then you pay." Heiner's mimicry dripped acid. "How I know if first you sell, then you don't pay?"

"No, sir," Jacob said, earnestly, "that's stealing. I wouldn't do that."

"How I know I don't kiss my basket goodbye?"

"But I promise I'll pay," Jacob pleaded. "I promise!"

"How old you, crazy kid?"

"Fifteen."

"Fifteen! You ain't even legal!" Heiner's wrath exploded. "God in Heaven!" he shrieked as his pounding fists underlined his words. "The kid's fifteen, never sold a nickel's worth, got no money, blind. Wants to be businessman and he thinks I'm crazy." He jumped to his feet, temper at full blast. "Get out of my shop, an' don't slam the door when you leave."

Defeated, Jacob turned and began tapping his way to the door. The long months of humiliating refusal flashed through his mind and he realized he had lost his last chance. Clenching his fists, he swung around. "I'm blind, but I'm not an idiot and I'm honest. If you can't trust me, you can't trust anybody in this world."

Heiner sank heavily into his chair and sighed deeply. "You crazy kid. But you stubborn." His grudging admission was tinged with admiration. "So, who knows, maybe you good salesman. Okay, so Kurt Heiner will be crazy, too." He walked over to the wall, selected a basket filled with cartons of matches and brought it to the astonished boy.

"Here," he said, "pay when you sell. Now get out of my shop and let me do my business."

Faga was chopping onions for their Sabbath supper when Jacob strutted into the kitchen, swinging the basket like a triumphal banner. "I've got it, Mama," he shouted, "I've got it!"

"Thank you, God." Faga murmured. She lifted her arm to her eyes and, with her sleeve, wiped away her tears. Supper that evening was a celebration honoring the new entrepreneur.

Louis bought the first box of matches.

CHAPTER 8

Sharp winds and piercing cold were Jacob's constant companions. As he fought the icy stairways, trudging from building to building and door to door, he earned three cents the first day, seventy-four cents the first week.

Though his earnings were disappointing, he quickly got the "feeling" of Chicago. He learned it was a city of apartment buildings crowded together like the matches in his box, separated only by fences or narrow walkways running along the sides of the buildings to the back doors.

He discovered it was easy to determine if a building was two or three stories high and the number of flats within it by first finding and counting the mailboxes in the entryway.

Locating stairways was easy enough, climbing them was not. They were dangerous obstacle courses, sometimes broken or with missing steps. He learned children and stairs were as natural a combination as air and water. The children used them for playgrounds and left toys strewn about. Families found them useful for storage or garbage areas. His cane became the antenna that guided him through the unknown perils each stairway presented.

Often he smiled to himself as he thought back to the match lady's gentle warning, words that had so completely escaped him at the time. "There are endless stairs and dogs and children." She was right. The stairs were endless. One day, curious, he counted them as he climbed and when the numbers stretched into the hundreds in a single hour, he stopped counting.

He could manage stairs but the dogs...! There were only two kinds, friendly or belligerent. He could pat the friendly dog and speak softly to it. But he soon discovered that speaking softly to a belligerent dog or trying to bluff his way past by ignoring it was dangerous. After his screams brought his rescue by the owner of an overly zealous watchdog holding his ankle in its mouth, Jacob never again ignored a belligerent dog.

Within the first few weeks he realized his real handicap was neither stairs nor dogs nor children nor his lack of sight. Because his eyes were open and looked normal, people believed he was pretending to be blind. Since people believed he was faking blindness, he decided that was exactly what he would do. Jacob began crossing his eyeballs and rolling them up and down. The trick worked and his earnings slowly increased.

Each evening, arriving home shortly before suppertime, he emptied his pockets on to a towel that Faga fastidiously placed over the tablecloth. The money was counted and deposited in a special jar wrapped with heavy string to make it recognizable for Jacob and placed in a corner of the pantry.

No matter how Jacob pleaded, Faga refused to take even one nickel. "No," she said firmly, "first you pay four dollars to Mr. Heiner, then we see."

It took thirty-two working days to accumulate the four dollars. Louis divided the pennies into four bags of one hundred each, took them to the bank and wheedled four crisp, new one-dollar bills from the teller.

Kurt Heiner had long ago written off his basket as a loss. When Jacob walked into his shop he was dumbfounded.

"God in Heaven," he gasped. "It's the crazy, blind kid."

Jacob smiled. "Yes," he replied, "the crazy, blind kid is here to pay his debt." He held out the four crisp dollar bills. "Here is the money I owe you."

"I don't expect..." Heiner mumbled, still in shock.

"I promised."

"Sure, sure. Many promise, but few pay. You okay, kid. You, I believe. So, is good. Take what you need, pay when you can. You not crazy kid. You okay business man."

The April thaw came early. Jacob was happy to see the rains replace the blizzards that had so often kept him fretting at home. Henry fashioned a waterproof cover for his basket that kept his matches dry, but his old raincoat didn't do the same for him. Each evening his soggy clothes decorated kitchen chairs so they could dry beside Faga's ancient, wood burning stove.

Spring brought some relief from the rains, but Jacob grew increasingly discontented as his sales earned more money for Kurt Heiner than for himself. When he confronted Heiner with his complaint, the big man roared with delight. "So!" he exclaimed, "now you real businessman. Next door is my friend Mueller. He has for you brushes, all kinds. Come, I go with you. I tell him you okay kid."

Brushes carried a greater margin of profit. Working from early morning until after dark he was soon earning a minimum of three dollars a day. But he grew depressed. He disliked selling. It was humiliating and unsatisfying. The future stretched before him as an endless conveyor belt of baskets going nowhere. He longed to open a shop to escape the stairs, the dogs, the weather and daily dangers he faced. But he lacked the capital.

At Jacksonville he had learned to play several band instruments by ear. Now he tried to get a job with small bands. But unable to read music, that door was closed to him.

He spent hours painfully familiarizing himself with the halls, corridors and elevators of several large commercial buildings and then applied for the job as a guide. The managers received him brusquely. A blind guide, tapping his way about, was hardly the professional image they wished to present to the public.

"I tried a number of things," Jacob wrote to a friend, "and failed in all of them."

By chance he met a woman who was earning an excellent living through the practice of Mechano-Therapy, which was similar to osteopathy. When she told him that she had learned the technique through a correspondence course and assured him he could practice as well as she, Jacob was elated. "I seized upon it," he recalled, "as a drowning man clutches at a straw." Perhaps this was the answer to his childhood dream.

Ever since the kind man with the gentle hands and soothing voice had stopped his tummy ache at the age of four, Jacob dreamed that he would become a doctor and stop people's pain. Even after he learned doctors must have eyes, his dream refused to die. Through the years he had never allowed the dream to surface, for he was convinced no medical school would accept a blind student. Even if such a miracle came to pass, he did not believe that he was capable of becoming a doctor. But Mechano-Therapy was a related field and required only hands, not eyes, and he had good hands. Perhaps this was the answer to his dream. At least it was worth a try.

In 1919, in response to a magazine request for his autobiography, he wrote, "I went home full of hope. If someone had told me that I could drive a steam engine, I would have had the same hope and would have felt like trying it.

"I applied to the American College of Mechano-Therapy, which promptly accepted my application and tuition with no questions asked. I sold brushes and matches until noon, then attended classes in the afternoon and evening.

"It was not a happy experience, for my fellow classmates laughed and jeered at my efforts. I felt very alone and out of place, and prayed that all would come out right. I hired a young Japanese student named Yamaguchi to read the lessons to me. I at once grasped the work and had no problem with examinations.

"The course lasted only a few months. At the graduation ceremony I was handed my diploma. Running my fingers across it, I discovered it had no writing on it, that it was completely blank. When I questioned my teacher, he was very embarrassed and told me a diploma cost fifteen dollars and the school didn't think I could get that much. Besides, they didn't think that being blind I'd ever notice it.

"I went right out, earned that fifteen dollars and got my diploma properly inscribed. Now I was a fully certified therapist, but when I tried to practice it, I realized how little I knew. The course had given me no practical experience, and I knew it was not the answer I sought."

Several days later, a chance remark changed his life.

While riding a streetcar on his way to selling in a new neighborhood, a man seated directly behind him told his companion "I'm going to the Bennett Typewriter Company. They're looking for salesmen. Maybe this time I'll be lucky."

Jacob whipped around. "Excuse me," he said. "I couldn't help overhearing what you said about the typewriter company. I'm looking for a job, too. Would you allow me to go with you?"

The man laughed. "Kid," he said, "you haven't a chance. They want men."

"I'd still like to try," Jacob insisted.

"Hell, it's a free country, kid. Nobody can stop you from trying."

"Would you let me go with you? It would be a lot easier for me because, you see, I'm blind."

He waited anxiously for the reply. There was an awkward silence. Jacob's keen ears caught the men's mumbled reluctance.

"Look," he said, "I don't want to cause you any trouble. Just give me the address and..."

"Nah, we'll take you. But you're wasting your time. Nobody's gonna hire a blind kid. What the hell, come on with us. It's the second stop from here."

Jacob and his newfound friends joined the large group of men waiting to be interviewed. When Jacob's turn came, the man grabbed his arm, "Kid," he grinned, "you're okay. I hope you get the job."

The personnel manager stared incredulously at the boy standing before him with a basket of brushes. He waited in stunned silence until Jacob announced, "Sir, I would like to work for your company."

"How old are you," the manager demanded.

"Sixteen."

"Sixteen? Sixteen." The manager shook his head in disbelief. Jacob waited. "What's the cane for? You blind?"

"Yes, sir. I'm blind."

"My God," the manager muttered. "What makes you think you can sell typewriters?"

"I know I can sell typewriters," Jacob insisted. "I've been selling door-to-door all over Chicago for over a year. I'm a good salesman. All I ask is a chance to show what I can do."

The manager studied Jacob, skeptically. He noted the clear, brown eyes, the confident stance, the determination. Finally, he spoke. "You've got spunk. I like that. All right, you'll have the chance you want for thirty days. If we don't like your record at the end of the month, you're out. Is that fair enough, kid?"

"Yes, sir!" Jacob could hardly restrain his elation. "That's fair enough."

At the turn of the century, typewriters were not common office equipment. Jacob found the field wide open. Working from ten to twelve hours a day, he compiled an impressive sales record. At the end of his trial month, he brought his records and receipts to the company's sales manager. That done, he stood anxiously aside awaiting the verdict. But the harried manager turned away without a word. Several endless moments ticked by before the manager noticed the boy was still there.

"Do you have a question?" he asked.

"Yes, sir." Jacob swallowed hard. "Do I keep the job or do you want the typewriter back?"

"Damn it," the man slapped his fist down upon the desk. "I forgot. I'm sorry, Bolotin, the president wants to see you. Go talk to him." Seeing Jacob's stricken face, he added warmly, "Good luck, kid."

A chill ran through Jacob. If he was to keep the job, this official would have known. Being sent to the president had only one meaning. He was going to be fired. He was a failure. But he had tried. He had tried hard.

Holding his head firmly erect to hide his despair, he forced himself to knock on the heavily paneled door. Mr. Bennett, a florid, heavy-set man with a thick golden chain dangling from his vest pocket, met Jacob at the door. "Come in, young man," he boomed. "I want to talk to you. Sit down right there." He seated Jacob solicitously and gave him a fatherly pat on his shoulder. "So you're our blind salesman."

"Yes, sir." Jacob replied, totally unprepared for such a welcoming approach.

"And you're all of sixteen years old, is that right?"

"Yes, sir."

"Well, well," Bennett laughed heartily as he seated himself behind his desk. "That's mighty young to be selling typewriters. Tell me, young man, do you like working for me?"

Jacob's spirit leaped. Perhaps there was still a chance. "Yes, sir. I do, very much, sir. Will you give me another chance?"

Bennett was puzzled. "Another chance?" Suddenly, he understood. "Good Lord," he chuckled. "Did you think I was going to fire you?"

Jacob nodded. "When they told me to see you, I thought..."

"Bolotin," the president interrupted, "I want you to know you were ninth from the top in sales this month. That's a hell of a good record, especially for a beginner. We're mighty proud of you, son. Just keep sales rolling in like that and you'll always have a job with Bennett's."

At last, Jacob had a secure, well-paying job. Though both Faga and Louis remonstrated with him, he kept out only the small amount of money he needed to pay his daily expenses, turning the rest over to them. It gave him enormous pleasure to know that his mother no longer had to decide between paying bills or feeding her family. He basked in the joy it gave his parents to buy needed clothing for his brothers and sisters and to replace a few pieces of badly worn furniture.

Still, peace eluded him. His yearning to study medicine consumed him. He tried to hide his growing unhappiness.

Louis was not fooled. He waited until they were sitting alone on the back porch, seeking a bit of coolness on a hot, muggy, summer evening, and said gently, "Something troubling you, Jake. Would you like to talk?"

With a rush, Jacob's emotional armor collapsed. "Papa," he cried, "I want to be a doctor."

"A doctor!" Louis was incredulous.

"Yes, Papa, more than anything else in the world, a doctor."

"How?" Louis asked, bitterly. The knowledge of his helplessness overwhelmed him. Suddenly he felt old and tired. "You know it is impossible," he replied, wearily.

"Impossible?" Jacob repeated. "No, Papa. I don't know that."

Louis gently tried to bring his son back to reality. "Jake, be sensible. You have good job, fine job. They like you."

"But, I don't like selling. Papa, what difference does it make if it's matches or brushes or typewriters? I'm still peddling door-to-door."

"My son," Louis said softly, "when you were a baby, your mama and I worried you would have to beg on street corners. Now, with God's help, you're making good money, earning more than your papa!" He placed his arm around Jacob's shoulder. "Mama and me are proud and happy for you, Jake. You should be happy too."

"Papa, please try to understand, I can never be happy selling. I want to be a doctor."

"Jake, think, think! Doctors must have eyes. Who will come to a blind doctor? What hospital will hire a blind doctor?"

"I don't know, Papa. I don't know. I only know that I must try."

Louis sighed, deeply. "So," he said, filled with tenderness for his blind son, "so you must try." He paused, then added deliberately, "Medical school expensive. Will take years, not months, like your therapy school. You'll have to give up good job. How will you pay for it?"

"No, Papa," Jacob bubbled with enthusiasm, "I won't have to give up my job. There's a school, the National Medical School, that offers courses only at night, no afternoon classes. It'll even be easier than the therapy school. Don't you see, Papa? That means I can keep on selling typewriters all day, just like I do now, and study real medicine at the same time."

Louis masked his concern. "That means long, hard days for anybody. Maybe it would be too..."

"No, Papa," Jacob broke in, happily. "I know I can do it. At least I have to try."

His spirit soared. By the end of summer he would be a student of medicine.

CHAPTER 9

Throughout the September day that marked the opening of enrollment week at the National Medical School in Chicago, Jacob had been in a state of euphoria. Scarcely aware of the dismal, blustery weather, punctuated by intermittent showers, he radiated such warmth and joy that sales were unusually brisk. He decided to stop early and rush home for a bath and change of clothing to make himself presentable at the university.

Faga insisted that he must eat some hot food before leaving, at least a bowl of her good lentil soup. At the table, Jacob surprised his family by suddenly springing to his feet, lifting his glass of tea and exclaiming, dramatically, "Why is this night different from all other nights?" the traditional question asked by the youngest child at the Passover ceremonial dinner. There was laughter as the family shouted their replies.

"Because tonight you're going back to school."

"Because you had a good supper for a change."

"Because you're going to be a doctor."

Louis lifted his arm for silence. When quiet was restored, he rose to his feet and said proudly, "Because, my son, tonight begins your real future."

"Yes," Jacob beamed at his family, "but most of all because tonight my dream is no longer just a dream. Tonight, it will start coming true."

When he arrived at the school, he found the lobby noisy and crowded with exuberant, would-be doctors. He stood for a moment, uncertainly, just inside the door. A student, wearing a heavy varsity sweater, noted the cane, the bewilderment, the hesitancy. He approached Jacob and asked casually, "You enrolling?"

"Yes," Jacob turned eagerly toward the voice.

"Good, me too. They're registering in room 106. Come on. Let's go." He took Jacob's arm and deftly steered him across the hall and down the long busy corridor.

Grateful for the unexpected kindness, Jacob murmured, "This is sure nice of you."

"Nah," his new friend scoffed. "I've got a sister that's blind. Something went wrong with her eyes when she was a kid. You, too?"

Jacob shook his head. "No, born that way."

"That's a tough break, fella. You've sure got guts enrolling in med school."

Reaching room 106, the young man asked, "What's your last name begin with?"

"B," Jacob answered, puzzled.

"Okay, you'll have to get in line right here for letters A-M. I'm a W. I go to table two. There's a guy behind the table giving out registration forms. He'll tell you what to do. Good luck, fella."

The harassed official behind the table was engrossed in distributing the forms and intoning monotonously, "Fill them out and leave them with the registrar."

When Jacob's turn came, he felt the precious papers thrust into his hand. "Is there someone I can dictate my answers to?" he asked.

"Of course not. Just write them down like everybody else."

"I can't," Jacob said. "I'm blind."

The official paused, his hands in mid-air. "What did you say?"

"I'm blind," Jacob repeated.

Stupefied, the man stared blankly at Jacob. "We don't accept blind students," he said. His tone ended the matter.

"I would like to try," Jacob persisted.

"There's no way," the official replied, thoroughly shaken, "no way at all for a blind person to take our courses." He made it more emphatic. "You'd be wasting your tuition. Step aside, please."

Jacob would not be put off. "It isn't important about the tuition. I'll pay extra tuition if you'll give me the chance."

The man was annoyed. "It isn't up to me," he snapped. "It's up to the board of trustees. They'll make the decision." He dismissed Jacob. "Leave your name, address and previous education with the clerk over there. We'll let you know. Now, move along." Then realizing, he added lamely, "Turn left, the desk is just about four or five steps straight ahead."

Jacob found the desk, gave the dumbfounded clerk the information, left discouraged and disconsolate in a downpour that matched his mood. As the days passed with no word from the school, his gloom deepened.

Returning from work a week later, his mother met him at the door and flung her arms about him. "Jake! Jake! The letter! The letter from the school!"

Jacob's body became rigid. "Is it yes or no?"

"It is yes!" Faga wept happily. "You're going to be a doctor."

Many times during the year Jacob wondered if her prophecy would come true. His courses were difficult and involved, far more than he had thought possible. With each passing month, he fought harder to maintain the rigid, difficult routine that he had established out of necessity. Promptly at 8:00 AM, he began traveling around the city's commercial districts selling typewriters. While four or five hours a day proved sufficient to earn his tuition and expenses, he worked extra hours for the additional money necessary to help support his family. His parents objected vehemently, but Jacob knew all too well how much they needed the money he provided. At 5:00 PM, he rushed home for a quick supper, leaving himself only enough time to tap his way from the trolley to the school, down the corridor and into his classroom moments before 7:00. Often, when sales kept him busy until after 6:00, it was too late to go home. With no food, except the sandwich Faga had packed for his lunch, he went directly to the school.

The last class ended at 10:00 PM. At that hour, the streetcars ran only every 30 to 40 minutes. By hurrying as fast as he was able, he could make the 10:30 trolley. But if he missed it as he often did and had the long wait for the 11:00 car, he reached home long after midnight. Faga always had some food prepared, which he devoured hungrily. Sleep was still hours away.

Unable to take notes like sighted fellow students, he had to remember each professor's lecture in its entirety, a Herculean task that required intense, exhausting concentration. With the lectures still fresh in his mind, he spent hours transcribing them into a notebook with his Braille stylus. Sleep was an enemy to be fought. Often, he lost the battle. Awakening with a start moments or hours later, he would berate himself furiously for having lost irreplaceable study time. No matter how late he finally went to bed, he rose at 5: 00 AM to put in two hours of study before kissing Faga goodbye and traveling to his selling area for the day.

Lack of food and sleep, the physical exertion of lugging the heavy, clumsy typewriter that seemed to grow heavier day by day, marching through the endless corridors of office buildings and factories, took its inevitable toll. As his exhaustion increased, he drove himself mercilessly to maintain the high level of sales and academic work he demanded of himself.

Suddenly, without warning, only weeks before the end of his first school year, his dream dissolved into a nightmare. Walking from the streetcar to the school he was surprised to find the way blocked by milling groups of angry students. As he tried to work his way to the entrance, a bitter voice called out, "Hey, guy, no use going in there anymore."

"Yeah," responded a voice hollow with defeat "We've had it."

"But I've got to," Jacob was puzzled. "I've got to get to class."

A chorus of loud, derisive laughter erupted and a bass voice sang out, "There ain't gonna be no class no more."

The May evening was warm and muggy, yet Jacob felt shivers rise up his spine. He recognized the presence of a classmate and turned to him for help. "Ben, what's wrong?" he asked, his voice tight with anxiety. "Is it true? No class tonight?"

"Yep."

"Why?"

"Because our great state health department has given us all a swift kick in the butt."

Jacob shook his head. "I still don't understand. What has the health department to do with this school?"

"Everything, Jake, everything. The bastards withdrew accreditation. All our classes here are worthless…a whole year not worth a damn."

"No, no!" Jacob heard himself screaming, "They can't do that! It's a mistake!"

"No mistake, Jake, no mistake." Jacob recognized the voice of one of his teachers. "It's done." He placed an arm around Jacob's shoulder. "Let's face it, Jake, the school is closed. I've lost my job, and you've lost a year of work."

"And," Jacob muttered miserably, "a year of tuition."

How he reached home that night always remained a mystery. His thoughts were in turmoil as he relived the unbelievable difficulties of the year he had endured. The exhausting struggle against time and sleep, scratching for every tuition dollar, battling to study medicine in spite of his handicap—all were irretrievably lost. Friends and family urged him to give up the ridiculous, unachievable dream, but quitting was as impossible for Jacob as ever seeing the sun.

"Don't worry," he told them, "only a worm can't fall. I'll get up again."

Jacob's buoyant optimism soon returned. Where others saw the lost year as a catastrophic defeat, he saw it as a shining plus because it had revealed to him inner capabilities that he did not know he had. And it had given him the confidence that he could indeed study medicine. The only questions were how and where. His money was gone. It would take years to see him through the solidly accredited school he had chosen, the prestigious Chicago College of Medicine and Surgery, [later to become Loyola University School of Medicine]. He also knew he would not be able to continue selling while attending school. He realized medicine could never be mastered in night classes but required all day attendance with full semester workloads.

There was only one solution. He had to earn enough to finance his education through the sale of typewriters. He went to see Mr. Bennett. "Sir, I am asking your permission to travel to other states to make my sales."

Bennett was stunned, "Why, Bolotin? You've been doing very well right here. Why do you want to go on the road?"

"Because," Jacob had rehearsed it carefully, "I'm going back to medical school."

"Medical school?" Bennett snorted. "I thought you'd given up that absurd idea long ago."

"No, sir. I've been attending night classes this year so I could work days. Now I know I have to go to a real university and carry full, daytime classes. I can't do that until I've earned my tuition for the entire four years."

"You can do that right here in Chicago. It's a big city." Bennett chomped heavily on his cigar. "If you like, I'll give you some suburbs to work in."

"Thank you, Mr. Bennett, but you have a lot of salesmen in the city and some already in the suburbs. If you will let me go into other states, I'll have the whole country in which to sell."

"Bolotin," Bennett exploded, deeply concerned, "you don't realize what you're asking for. Going on the road is tough. It's a lonely, backbreaking, miserable job, even for salesmen with eyes. For you, it's an absolute impossibility."

Jacob felt sick. Bennett meant well, but he had to make him understand. "Sir," he said, "I know that for me many things are impossible, but not medicine. The past year at night school has taught me that I can study medicine. I can become a doctor. I know it will be hard."

"A hell of a lot harder for you than for any of the other students."

"But I'm not afraid of work. Going on the road will give me sales I can't make here, and every sale means dollars added towards my tuition."

"You're really serious, aren't you?"

"Yes, sir."

Bennett made no reply. Instead, he began noisily shuffling papers on his desk.

Jacob was worried. Had he been dismissed? He stood motionless, fearful that he would betray his anxiety. Finally, when Bennett still remained silent, he asked softly, "Sir?"

"Damn it, Bolotin," Bennett burst out, "how in God's name will you find your way on trains around strange towns and places you can't see?"

Jacob smiled. "I travel all around Chicago in strange neighborhoods and strange buildings. If I can do that, I can get around anywhere. I'm not afraid, sir."

"Well, maybe you're not afraid, but I am. Look, Bolotin, I'm a businessman. I can't take responsibility if you get hurt or God knows what out there."

"If I get hurt, Mr. Bennett, the responsibility is mine, not yours. Please don't worry, sir. I can take care of myself."

Bennett sat back, the cigar dangling from his lips momentarily forgotten. "Yes," he acknowledged, "I believe you can. Yes indeed, I believe you can." His words came slowly, as if he was seeing Jacob for the first time. "I've got to say it, you're quite a boy. Boy? Hell, you're a man, a man I respect."

Suddenly, Jacob's crushing tension vanished and he felt thirty feet tall.

"All right, Bolotin, you can go on the road. The clerk will give you the list of cities covered by our other salesmen. The rest of the country, every damn inch of it, it's all yours. Just, for God's sake, be careful."

CHAPTER 10

It took Jacob four years. Every year on the road earned almost a full year's tuition. By living frugally, staying in cheap hotels or rooming houses, restricting himself to the barest necessities and, wherever possible, hiring wagon drivers to take him from town to town to save train fare, he managed to save most of his monthly paycheck. This he mailed to Faga, who painstakingly divided it according to Jacob's instructions. Two-thirds was his, deposited in the bank for tuition. The remaining one-third was hers for household expenses.

But Faga's heart ached for her blind son in his self-imposed exile. She longed for his quick return home and prayed day and night for divine protection from the constant dangers he faced. By careful skimping, she succeeded in funneling at least one-half of her share into Jacob's account. It was a delightful secret that the whole family enjoyed. Especially Fred. His concern for his "little brother" often kept him awake nights. Determined to help Jacob, he decided to quit his job at the livery stable and go into business for himself.

With money borrowed from cousin Harry, he opened a small shop and stocked it with janitorial supplies on consignment from Mueller's Brush Shop. The little shop prospered from the beginning. Fred quickly discovered he had stumbled into a service greatly needed in the rapidly growing city. By the year's end the proud "big brother" was able to make small deposits into Jacob's bank account, a secret he shared only with Faga.

For Jacob, the passing years seemed endless. Sternly repressing his impatience, Jacob traveled throughout the United States and sold typewriters in every state in the Union. Life on the road was arduous and beset with difficulties. Bennett's grim warning often echoed and re-echoed in his mind. "It's lonely, back-breaking, miserable work." Yes, it was all that, but for him it was more, far more.

Locked in his dark world, burdened by the heavy, bulky typewriter of his day, Jacob was entirely dependent upon his indispensable cane. But a piece of wood is neither wise nor prophetic. It could not always find the cracked, toe-catching gaps in sidewalks, the loose or broken boards in wooden walks, the slimy holes in deeply rutted mud streets. It could not warn him of running children or dogs underfoot. His body bore the bruises and aching pains of the hundreds of times he slammed into posts, walls, trees or people, sprawled head-long on the ground, tumbled down stairs or fought his way across mud-soaked streets.

He sweated through the sweltering Midwestern summers, when the hot prairie winds scorched man and beast, and shivered through the fierce wintry cold of mountain states. The winters were the hardest. Heavy snowfalls deadened the sound of approaching horses, distorted the closeness of oncoming wagons, hid curbs and crossings and often camouflaged streets and steps with treacherous patches of ice that sent him sliding helplessly as his feet went out from under him.

Gradually he developed an uncanny awareness of potential dangers, an intense, instinctive radar that sensed the nearness of fences, buildings, trees, and stopped him inches before bumping into them. His ears became more keenly attuned to even distant sounds and could accurately determine the proximity of people or animals.

He thought he knew what it meant to be blind in a sighted world, but traveling through the cities, towns and crossroad settlements of North America, the enormity of his handicap became blazingly clear. Even basic human needs became monumental problems. It never occurs to the sighted, when entering a room, to be concerned with the position of furniture, doors, windows. Finding the bathroom down the hall requires neither thought nor effort. For Jacob these simple things could be huge obstacles. Wherever he lodged for the night, he had to memorize the location of the front door, the number of steps to the stairway to his room, the length of each hallway, the placement of furniture both in his room and in the lobby, the number of doors between his room and the bathroom. If he was lucky it would be an inside bathroom. But often in the places he could afford only outdoor plumbing was available. He discovered privies were almost always located at the end of primitive paths that made reaching them hazardous journeys into the unknown.

Selling typewriters was the least of his problems. Prospective buyers were impressed by his dexterity in handling the "newfangled contraption." Certainly if it was so obviously simple for a blind man to operate, it could be easily mastered by people with good eyes. It amused Jacob that it was actually his lack of sight that clinched the sale.

By the end of four years he had achieved one of the highest salaries paid by the Bennett Typewriting Company to any of its employees. Yet for Jacob, the time had come to leave the firm. Mr. Bennett refused to accept his resignation. "Bolotin," he said, "don't be hasty. Think it over."

"I have, sir. I've thought it over very carefully."

"Look, Bolotin," the president persisted, "you are one of our top salesmen. We don't want to lose you. Stay with us. We'll give you a really substantial raise in salary."

"Thank you, sir, but I have almost enough now to see me through medical school."

"Come now, Bolotin," Bennett was vastly amused, "You know that is absolute nonsense. Who ever heard of a blind doctor?" Jacob was silent. "Damn it, Bolotin, don't be a fool. Look, if it's money you want, we'll increase your commission as well."

"That's a very generous offer and I'm grateful, sir, but I worked these last four years for one reason, to be able to study medicine. Now I'm ready to begin."

"For God's sake, Bolotin, be sensible. You're making good money here. Be realistic. You'll never be admitted to any medical school and even if you are, how can you study without eyes?"

"I will find readers. My friends will help me."

"Friends? You're a fool if you count on friends. Oh, sure, they'll promise, but they won't stick to it. And even if, by some miracle, you do become a doctor, what hospital is going to allow you to practice? Why would any patient choose you when Chicago is filled with damn good sighted doctors. Be practical, Bolotin, you're a top-notch salesman, our best. We don't want to lose you. You don't need eyes to sell typewriters. We're offering you a substantial raise in salary and a higher commission. What's more, we'll give you any territory that you want. You can choose whatever you want. Why give up a good job for some idiotic dream?"

"An idiotic dream? Yes," Jacob replied, gravely, "maybe it is, Mr. Bennett. Maybe I will never become a doctor. But I have to try. Nothing can stop me from trying."

Abruptly, Bennett rose and approached Jacob. "I've never known anyone like you." He paced his words slowly, thoughtfully. "You've been a helluva good salesman. With your guts, you'll make a helluva good doctor. But," he paused and then added, earnestly, "if you don't, if things go wrong, remember, you'll always have a job in this firm."

As Jacob murmured his thanks and started toward the door, Bennett stopped him. "Wait just a moment." He strode from the room, returning almost instantly. "Bolotin," he said, "there is a new model typewriter waiting for you at the front desk."

Jacob was overwhelmed, but Bennett brushed aside his thanks. "No, the thanks are ours, Bolotin, for the job you've done." He clasped Jacob's hand and pressed it, warmly. "But there is something you can do for me."

Jacob was deeply moved and replied huskily, "Of course, sir, anything."

"Don't forget to invite me to your graduation."

CHAPTER 11

He was free! Free to follow his dream. Jacob was ecstatic. He even allowed himself, for the first time in his life, the heady luxury of buying gifts for his parents' anniversary. With the secret help of his sisters, Emma and Bessie, he selected an embroidered blouse for Faga and a woolen sweater for Louis.

Displaying the gifts to the family, Jacob announced happily. "When I become a famous doctor, I'll buy new clothes for everybody."

"No, you won't!" The childish voice spoke loudly, sending a chill through the room. Startled, Faga turned to face the six-year-old neighbor from the flat below.

"Becky, please!" Faga cried.

"My mama said Jake can never be a doctor," the child prattled on unperturbed. "'Cause doctors have to see and Jake can't. He's blind."

"Becky, time you go home," Faga said sharply, with a quick glance at Jacob who stood rigidly transfixed, the clothing hanging from his arms. She forced herself to speak calmly. "And tell your mama she wrong. Jake will be a doctor."

The child ambled slowly across the room. "My mama is never wrong," she said firmly, slamming the door behind her.

Faga turned to her son and gently transferred the clothing into her own arms. Jacob didn't move. "How children talk!" she said airily. "Pay no attention. Mrs. Gold is wrong, and her Becky's wrong."

"No, they're right," Jacob said. His joy had vanished into the cold blast of reality. "You know it and I know it. If you believe I can become a doctor, then you are as blind as I am."

Jacob was plunged into despair. Doubts assailed him. An innocent child had revealed his cherished dream as the mirage it was. Everyone knew the truth, had known it all these years. In his vanity and arrogance he had persisted in living a lie. How could he have believed he would become a doctor? No patient would trust him. No hospital would accept him. Why would anyone seek a doctor without eyes when there was a city full of doctors with eyes? He knew the questions as he knew the answers. It was idiocy to have thought such goals possible for a blind man. He was a fool for leaving Bennett's. He would go back, admit his stupidity and ask for his old job again. For days, he hesitated, delayed, and finally realized he could never make himself go back.

Despondent, bitterly dejected, he took up his long forgotten basket of brushes and resumed selling door-to-door.

As the burning days of summer flowed into the crisp coolness of fall, Jacob's despair deepened. The knowledge that the university had begun enrollments tormented him. His agony increased as he found himself selling in areas surrounding the school.

The day before the enrollment period ended had been hellish. The relentless sun had pursued him, baked him. The oppressive heat had fought him in stifling hallways and doubled back upon him from sidewalks and building walls. People were irritable. Ugly remarks slapped at him. Doors slammed in his face. He had not made enough sales to earn grocery money for his mother. During the long ride home, he berated himself. He had been at fault, not the sun. He had concentrated upon his misery, not his work. Tomorrow he would sell far away from the school.

As he put his key in the door, it was flung open from inside. "Jake!" Faga cried, "Come in the kitchen, Papa has something to tell you!" She grabbed his basket and threw it aside. "This you won't need anymore."

Puzzled, Jacob allowed her to pull him into the kitchen. The family, gathered around Louis, were all speaking at once.

"Tell him, Papa! Tell him!"

"How can I tell," Louis shouted indignantly, "when you're all yelling and screaming?"

There was instant silence.

"All right. Now I talk. Jake, today there is a story in the newspaper about a big doctor with many patients. Babcock. Dr. Robert Hall Babcock."

"So?" Jacob asked. "There are a lot of doctors. What has that doctor to do with me?"

"Jacob, Dr. Robert Babcock is blind."

Suddenly, he wasn't tired. Suddenly, he wasn't hot. His despair evaporated. He felt a lightness he had never known. All the hopes he had repressed flooded through him.

There was still time. Enrollment was still open for another day. Tomorrow his new life would begin.

He was up with the morning sun. Too impatient to eat breakfast, he prowled restlessly from room to room as the long hours crawled by. When, at last, it was time to leave for the university, he startled Faga by asking for his basket of brushes.

"Why?" she demanded. "That you don't need anymore."

"Mama, today may be the most important day in my life and I will never need that basket again. But if I'm not accepted, if they say no..."

"They can't say no! There is already a blind doctor."

He took Faga in his arms and kissed her. "They can say it, Mama," he said softly. "They can say it, and if they do, I will not waste the day. I'll sell brushes. Now give me the basket."

His pulse raced with excitement as he entered the school and tapped his way around until he found the reception desk. The clerk was annoyed.

"Can't you read?" she snapped. "No beggars or salesmen allowed."

"I did not come to beg or sell. I came to enroll."

"Oh! Well, it's straight down that corridor to the registrar's office."

"I'm sorry to trouble you, but I'm blind. Would you please show me where the corridor is?"

The astounded clerk stared at the young man standing before her. She saw the cane, the basket, and the eyes that seemed to focus directly upon her.

"Come with me." She arose, placed her hand gently on his arm and led him to the registrar's office. Opening the door, she spoke in an uncertain voice.

"Dr. Clutton, this young man wishes to see you." She caught her breath. "I mean — he wishes to speak with you."

Clutton looked in amazement at the basket. "We don't need any brushes," he said edgily.

"No, no!" she assured him hastily. "He's not here to sell."

"I see." Clutton smiled. "Well then, how can I help you?"

"I wish to enroll."

Frantically, the clerk signaled Clutton and fled. His smile vanished. "Are you blind?" The question was sharp and blunt.

"Yes, sir."

"And you want to become a doctor?"

Jacob's body trembled, but he replied firmly, "Yes, sir. Very much, sir."

"You're the fellow Dr. Schroth told me about. He suggested we enroll you."

Schroth! Vivid memory flashed through Jacob's mind. The brilliant man who coached med students for exams. They had chatted briefly a few times, but Schroth had spoken about him to Clutton! Stunned, Jacob stood mute.

"Yes. Well, I was wondering if you'd actually show up. Let's see, your name is..."

Jacob heard the quick, impatient shuffling of papers.

"Oh, yes — here it is — BOLOtin. And you said you want to become a doctor?"

Still in shock, Jacob could only mumble, "Yes, sir. I believe I can do it."

"You're blind, and you believe you can do it?"

Clutton's unexpected mockery astounded Jacob. "Yes, sir," he repeated tightly, "I know I can do it."

"Oh! Now you know you can do it. Well, there's something else you should know. There's no way, no possible way," he emphasized the words again, "no possible way a blind man can make it."

Jacob couldn't see Clutton's icy stare, but he was puzzled by the overt hostility in the registrar's voice. Quietly, stubbornly, he fought back.

"Dr. Babcock made it. He's blind."

"Yes, well, that was years ago. Requirements were very different then. Easier. He'd never make it today, and neither will you."

"You don't know me." Fiercely he held back the anger that surged through him.

"No, I don't need to." Clutton replied smugly. "But I do know the study of medicine. It's no tea party. It's a long, hard four-year grind. Half of our would-be doctors with normal sight fail," Clutton continued derisively, "What makes you think you can do it?"

"I still want to try." Jacob's voice was steely calm.

"Try? That'll be a mighty expensive try. Tuition is not cheap. And," Clutton jeered, "you can't make it selling toothbrushes." The registrar was impatient. "Do you still wish to enroll?"

Yes! Jacob screamed inwardly. I went through four years of hell to reach this moment. He clenched his fists around his basket and forced himself to reply calmly, "Yes, I still wish to enroll."

"Very well. Just remember, that's your decision, not mine." He shoved some papers across the counter. "Here are the enrollment forms. My secretary, Miss Manning, will record your answers."

Across the room, Miss Manning saw Jacob groping for the papers. "Please," she jumped up, "let me get them." Gathering the forms, she gently seated Jacob beside her desk. "Let me take that basket. I'll just put it right down here." She placed it on the floor beside Jacob's chair. "It's not heavy," she observed with a little chuckle, "but I'll bet it gets pretty heavy lugging it around all day!"

Jacob smiled. "You're very perceptive."

"Not always," she laughed as she resumed her seat. "Let's get these papers filled out."

When he returned the completed forms, Clutton gave them a cursory glance. "All right, Mr. BOLOtin."

"We pronounce it Bo-LA-tin," Jacob corrected politely.

"Oh! Well! Pardon me, Mr. BoLAtin!"

Jacob winced at the exaggerated mimicry.

"Tuition is due tomorrow. It can be paid in full, or in installments. If a payment is late, you'll be asked to leave. Is that clear, Mr. BoLAtin?"

"Yes."

"Can you pay it?"

"It will be paid tomorrow — for the first year — in full."

"Oh! Well! In that case…" Clutton stuttered in shocked surprise, "you are enrolled. Classes begin in two weeks. But, I will tell you plainly," he said, making no attempt to hide his disdain, "we have no facilities for handicapped persons. If you keep up with the other students, well and good. If not, we'll ask you to leave. And do not ever come into any of these offices asking for special favors or privileges. They will not be granted. Do you understand?"

"Perfectly. Thank you."

Jacob turned and began tapping his way to the door.

"Wait! Just a minute, Mr BoLAtin! You forgot something."

Clutton signaled to Miss Manning. "Oh!" she gasped, "I'm sorry." She snatched up the basket and placed it in Jacob's hands. "My fault, sorry," she whispered.

"Yes! You'd better hang on to that basket!" Clutton's voice reeked with sarcasm. "You may be needing it again, sooner than you think."

Jacob turned back to the door, but Clutton wasn't finished.

"I think I'd better warn you again. Don't ever come asking for favors or special privileges. They will never be granted!"

Aflame with humiliation, seething with indignation, Jacob vowed he'd cut off his fingers one by one before he'd ever make such a request.

He never did.

But now, as he made his way down the long corridor, his heart sang. Even Clutton's cruel, hostile words were music to his ears. He had been accepted! He was enrolled! It was enough. Classes begin in two weeks. The words chimed sweetly in his head. Two weeks! At last he had reached the starting line.

Supper at the Bolotins that night was a joyous, noisy celebration as everyone lifted glasses of tea to toast the new doctor-to-be. Faga didn't join the celebrants. Humming happily to herself, she was busy passing around platters of food. She was bubbling with inner excitement. Louis knew the symptoms. She was up to something.

"All right, Fagale," he teased. "What you hiding?"

Faga giggled. "It's not what I hiding, it's what I giving away."

Now everyone was curious.

"Our broken chairs!" shouted Sarah.

"No."

"Your old bed?" Emma guessed.

"No!"

"The kitchen sink!" Fred yelled above the din.

"All right, Mama," Jacob joined the merriment. "What did you give away?"

"Your blue suit."

The merriment stopped abruptly. Louis sat stunned.

"Jake's good blue suit you give away?"

"Good?" Faga scoffed. "That old, worn-out suit? For five years Henry wore it. Then it goes four years with Jake on the road. That's enough already."

"But, Mama," Jacob protested softly, "I have only two suits."

"Yes," Faga replied, "and if you weren't wearing one, I'd give that away too."

"Wherever you give it," Louis was enraged, "tomorrow you go and take it back!"

"Can't," Faga smiled serenely. "This morning a beggar came. So, I give him food and Jake's suit."

"Well, Jake," Fred chortled, "guess you'll just have to go to school in your underwear."

"New underwear! Two new suits!" Faga said firmly.

There was a long, uneasy silence. Determined to end the discussion, Faga began busily clearing away the supper dishes. Louis broke the silence.

"Yes," he erupted angrily, "he needs new clothes but..."

"But we can't afford it!" Jacob sprang to his feet, his face twisted with worry. "Mama, you know we can't afford it."

"No," Faga smiled, "for Jake the Salesman we can't afford. But, for Jake the Doctor, with God's help, we will afford."

CHAPTER 12

On the opening day of school, he dressed carefully — new suit, new shirt, new shoes — the miracle of acceptance still singing in his heart. He congratulated himself on his foresight for having memorized the location of several classrooms when he had registered two weeks earlier. He tapped his way confidently to his first period classroom unaware of the curious stares of his fellow students. Once inside the door, he stopped, suddenly bewildered. Which way should he move? Right? Left? Forward? Where was the Professor's desk? Were there chairs or desks? Which way did they face? How were they arranged? Which were the empty ones?

As arriving students walked past him in the doorway, he listened intently to determine the direction of their footsteps, but the room was too noisy. He stood baffled and helpless. Abruptly the babble trickled away into stunned silence as the students gazed incredulously at the apparition with a cane in the doorway. A blind med student!

The professor seated at his desk saw Jacob's dilemma and quickly buried himself in his lecture notes. Clutton had warned the faculty about the arrogant Mr. Bo-LA-tin. They had agreed, the study of medicine was impossible for a blind man, and he would be accorded no special favors or assistance of any kind.

Now he said curtly, "Mr. Bolotin?"

"Yes, sir," Jacob answered eagerly.

"Please find a seat, I am ready to begin class."

Jacob steeled himself to ignore the unexpected hostility of both students and professor. At least the professor's few words had revealed the location of his desk and the direction the seats faced. Burning with embarrassment in the room's dead silence, he began moving slowly, probing with his cane for a seat.

Suddenly, a hand grasped his elbow and a voice close to him said softly, "There's a seat right here, fella, next to me. Come sit down."

Murmuring his thanks, Jacob sank gratefully into the empty chair, embarrassment forgotten as he struggled to grasp the reality of the moment. The impossible had come to pass. Here he was, actually sitting in this prestigious college, a full-fledged medical student.

His elation vanished quickly in his opening classes. With each professor's lecture, the gigantic problems confronting him stood sharply revealed. He was a medical student, but how was he going to study?

At the National Medical School he had nearly killed himself transcribing a single nightly lecture into Braille. Now he faced four to six lecture classes a day. Each professor assigned a text-book with pages to be read and thoroughly studied for the next day's class work. But reading was only a part of the problem. Sighted students had a wealth of outlines, pictures, charts and diagrams, all essential in preparation for examinations and class work. He could neither see nor draw anatomical charts or dia-grams. He could not use a microscope. A staggering amount of lab work and outside assignments were required. No medical textbooks were printed in Braille. The vast wealth of audio aids commonplace today were nonexistent.

He fought constantly to overcome the terrible frustration and sense of helplessness that welled up in him. They were like demons lurking behind every obstacle he faced. They had to be exorcised.

Failure was a certainty unless he could find someone to read lecture notes and textbooks aloud to him while he made notes in Braille. He appealed to friends who tried valiantly, but reading medical books was tedious and difficult. None of them could devote seven nights a week to the task indefinitely.

"I asked students who would talk to me and help me from room to room," Jacob wrote years later. "They agreed to read to me, but none seemed to want to do it continuously. I was very careful not to force myself onto anybody. As soon as I felt that one student seemed tired of reading, I thanked him for his assistance, saying that perhaps he had some special reading to do for himself. Then I would ask another of the boys to read for awhile."

It became quickly and painfully obvious that the haphazard assistance of a few sympathetic fellow students who had to sacrifice their own study time, or dependence upon friendship, would never provide the intensive daily reading that was his only key to graduation. He nearly failed his first examination because his reader had simply forgotten to come.

Panic-stricken, Jacob decided to call on Dr. Robert Hall Babcock. Here was the only blind man who had successfully become a physician. Babcock certainly had faced the same problems and had conquered them. Babcock would tell him what to do.

He obtained a three o'clock appointment. At two-thirty, glowing with anticipation, he entered Babcock's elegant reception room. Patients came and went, but he was not called. Bewildered, he sat and waited, doggedly determined to speak to the doctor. Finally, at five-fifteen, he was ushered into Babcock's office.

With pounding heart, Jacob introduced himself and explained why he had come. Babcock did not reply. Jacob sensed the man's hostility. He waited. When, at last, Babcock spoke, his words were brittle, cold, precise.

"What makes you think you can become a doctor without sight?"

"You did it, sir."

"It was different with me. I gradually lost my sight. I graduated in 1878, thirty years ago. Requirements were far less demanding then. There was little laboratory work, no competition, no license exam." He stopped abruptly. Then, stiffly, "Have you sufficient funds?"

"No, sir. I earn my way by selling door-to-door."

"I had wealthy parents who financed my education, read to me, hired guides to lead me, tutors to coach me. Nothing stood in my way."

"I am not afraid, sir. I know I can succeed if I learn how to study. Would you tell me how you…"

"Forget it!" Babcock snapped. "You are wasting your time and my time. You are wasting effort and money. Medical school is not for you. It is a futile, presumptuous dream. Continue selling. You will never become a doctor."

As he left Babcock's office humiliated, angry, his disappointment bitter and deep, Jacob vowed to prove Babcock wrong.

He hired nurses and students to read to him but, lacking motivation, they proved unreliable. Whenever one failed to appear an entire night's study was irretrievably lost, leaving him unprepared for the following day. Falling further and further behind, he knew it was only a matter of time before he would be forced to leave school.

Though he always insisted he did not believe in miracles, he had to admit that Herman Friedman's sudden entry into his life was nothing short of miraculous.

CHAPTER 13

One week later, walking to the streetcar after classes, Jacob became aware that someone had fallen into step beside him.

"Excuse me." The male voice was pleasant but heavily accented. "I go also to streetcar. Okay I walk with you?"

"Sure." Jacob was pleased. "Glad to have someone to talk to. My name is Jacob."

"Yah, I know. Jake Bolotin. Your name everyone in school knows."

Amazed, Jacob could only mumble, "Oh."

"Yah. You're the blind fella who wants to be doctor."

Jacob laughed. "That's me all right."

"I want also to be doctor. Many weeks I wait to talk with you. My name is Herman Friedman. I come not long ago from Poland. I have wife, five children and saloon. I don't want mine whole life selling beer."

Jacob laughed. "I understand. I sold typewriters."

"For you is hard in school because you have no eyes to read. I have eyes to read, but for me is hard because English is hard. In textbooks—many words I not understand."

"Right," Jacob nodded. "Some of those medical terms are real tongue twisters. I know exactly what you mean."

"Excuse me. You not know. English is for you your language. For me is Polish. Medical records I can learn, but English I not understand. When I come to America, I go to night school to become citizen, learn English language."

"You speak very well," Jacob interrupted.

"No, not like you. Newspapers I can read, but books in school, I not understand. I try—but is no good. I am failing."

"That makes two of us, Herman. I'm afraid I'll fail too, unless I find someone to read to me."

"You found! Me! I read to you," Herman's voice throbbed with excitement. "I help you! You help me! I read, you explain!"

The two men stood stock still facing each other. The street-car came and went. Neither noticed.

"You will read to me?" Jacob shook his head in disbelief. Was the sharp winter wind playing tricks on him? He took a deep breath and asked again, "You will read to me?"

"Yah! Yah! I will read if you explain and help me prepare for examinations. You will do that?"

The words were real! Herman Friedman was real "Yes!" Jacob shouted. "Yes, Herman, yes! Let's start tonight!"

For the next four years, the two students with widely differing backgrounds and handicaps, spent six hours every night studying together in the rear booth of Herman's saloon, constantly interrupted by customers.

"Hey, Hermie!" they would shout and bang their mugs on the table. "You ain't no doctor yet. Pour me a beer!"

"Dammit, Hermie! Get the lead out! We want some service here."

During the saloon's busy hours, Jacob helped Herman fill the orders. He soon learned to sell cigars by smelling the subtle differences in the brand odors and became so expert at drawing a good head of beer the customers often teased Friedman by yelling for Jake, not Hermie, to "Draw me a glass!"

But when studying for examinations, Herman brooked no nonsense. Whenever a hapless customer wandered in he announced firmly, "My beer is warm. Go across the street to Whitey's."

Often Herman's droning reading would lapse into silence punctuated by gargantuan snores. After allowing him a brief respite, Jacob would call out, "Read, Herman, read!" Snoring and reading played tag through the years.

Though Whitey's business prospered and Herman's dwindled to a trickle, Jacob now had a reader who was as motivated as he was. But the study battle was far from won. New threatening problems arose almost daily, requiring weeks of anguished searching with nerve-racking trial and error before solutions were found.

Then, in one of his classes, a seemingly insurmountable obstacle confronted him.

CHAPTER 14

Professor William Lowry Copeland, head of the department of anatomy, had lined his classroom and laboratory with large wall charts, each displaying one of the complex systems of the body. Skeletal charts posed no problem. "Old Elmer," the class skeleton, provided the perfect hands-on subject Jacob needed. His brain memorized every detail his sensitive fingers found as they explored size, shape and placement of even the tiniest bones and joints. By spending hours with "Old Elmer" and using his own body as a living model, he easily mastered bone structure.

"Elmer and I," he told Herman happily, "are practically on speaking terms."

But charts of the nine internal systems were monumental problems. All medical students were required to memorize them, but how could he memorize charts he could not see? While Professor Copeland, using a long pointer, traced the systems outlined on the charts in vivid colors, he sat fuming at his helplessness. After the second lecture, the professor called him aside.

"Bolotin," he began gently, "of course you know a doctor must have a thorough knowledge of every body system. You must find some way to learn them or..." his voice trailed off into silence. Then he plunged on, "I'm afraid...well, look, I'm sure you understand."

"Yes, sir. I know, and I've been trying to find the way... Sir, can you give me any suggestions?"

It was a moment before the professor found his voice. "I'm sorry," he replied softly. "I wish I could. I... I've never had anything like this before. I'm afraid you'll have to find the answer yourself."

"Oh, I will!" Jacob's smile belied his inner fear. "But," he hesitated, "I'll need time to..."

"You've got it, Bolotin. The chart exams will be in exactly eight weeks. That should give you plenty of time."

"Yes, sir. Thank you, Dr. Copeland."

As Jacob turned to leave the room, the professor patted his shoulder. "I'm sure you'll find the answer. So far, you've managed to find ingenious solutions to all your problems. I'm confident you'll solve this one, too."

Jacob was far from confident. He knew what lay behind Copeland's gentle words. Find the solution and memorize the charts or admit he had failed.

The only thing he did admit, as he rode the streetcar to Herman's saloon, was that the charts were an incredible challenge. But defeat? With Jacob's innate optimism such a premise was inconceivable. The solution existed—had to exist.

As the streetcar rattled and jounced, ideas rattled and jounced in his mind. Gradually he became aware there was something he should be remembering. Something nagged at his brain and fluttered just on the brink of recall. He knew intuitively it was the answer he sought. He dug deeply into memories of childhood, of Jacksonville, his years on the road, but whatever it was eluded him. It sat beside him in the booth with Herman, and the study session at the saloon that night was an abysmal failure. After four hours the habitually patient Herman finally exploded. "Go home, Jake!" he growled. "Go home! Tonight here you are sitting, but your head is not thinking. Go home!"

Faga was delighted to welcome her son home two hours early. "Jake," she said as she served the food she always had waiting for him in the kitchen. "Now you can pick instead of me."

"Pick what, Mama?"

"I knitting for you nice sweater. You pick which you like better. This...or this." She handed him two lengths of yarn.

Jacob slid his fingers up and down the pieces of yarn. "One is thick, one is thin." He ran the yarn through his fingers again. "Thick – thin!" He caught his breath in sudden excitement. "Mama, are there other kinds of yarn?"

"Of course, many kinds."

Shivers raced along his spine. "Mama, do you have any more here in the house?"

His excitement communicated itself to Faga. "Wait!" she exclaimed. Darting from the room, she returned with her knitting basket bulging with yarn. "Here," she said, "here is big and heavy for making blanket. Here is cotton, soft to crochet for the girls' pretty collars. But why?" she asked. "Why do you need yarn?"

Jacob could contain himself no longer. "For the charts, Mama! The charts! Now I can learn the charts!"

Faga clapped her hands. "Aha!" she laughed. "You mean like I make for you the little cards?"

Jacob sprang from his chair. "The animal cards! That's what I've been trying to remember! The animal cards! I'd forgotten all about them."

"Of course, you forget. You were only a baby, two—three years old."

"How did you do them, Mama?'

"Papa and I put on cards animal pictures. Each one I make different. Some I sew with thread, some I crocheted, some I knit. So! Now you are needing charts? I sew for you."

Jacob grabbed Faga and waltzed her around the table as they laughed and cried together.

He had the solution. Now all he needed were the charts.

"Sir," he asked Dr. Copeland after class, "where can I buy the anatomy charts?"

"Buy?" Copeland was amused. "That's not necessary. I have a stack of old ones I don't use any more. I'll give you all you need. Wait just a moment, I'll get them for you."

Jacob heard him rummaging in his office and counting softly to himself.

"Okay," he said as he emerged, "I'm sure I got all nine. But, just to make sure, let's check as I roll them up for you. Here we go: circulation, digestive, endocrine, integumentary." He paused, "What a fancy name for hair, skin and nails."

"I know," Jacob nodded. "I still have trouble pronouncing it."

"Sometimes we all do, Jake. Let's see, that was number four, now—muscular, nervous, respiratory, reproductive, urinary. That's it," he said as he tied them together, "all nine of them. Makes quite a load. Can you manage it?"

Jacob laughed, "I'm used to big loads, and this is nothing compared to the load you've taken off my mind. I'll do fine. Thank you, Dr. Copeland."

"I can't imagine how you'll use these," Copeland said as he opened the door for Jacob, "but I'm sure you do." Then he added, pleased, "I knew you would find the answer."

Faga commandeered a small battalion of friends. Within days, the women mounted the charts on heavy paper and began meticulously embroidering them with varying thicknesses and textures of yarn, silk and cotton thread.

Though the women tried valiantly, they were burdened with large families and household chores. Their slow progress worried Herman who knew the time limit was not going to change. Saying nothing to Jacob, he quietly spoke to several of their school friends who immediately volunteered to relieve Faga's ladies of the more complicated charts. They traced the charts on cardboard and outlined them with an ingenious assortment of wire, twine, string, and cord. One proudly supplied lengths of straw scrounged from a farmer.

Herman brought each completed chart to his saloon. After the nightly study session, Jacob took the chart home and sat up memorizing it in its minutest detail. If he was able to salvage two or three hours sleep, he considered it a happy bonus.

By examination time, he had caught up with the class.

CHAPTER 15

Jacob received an A on the anatomy exam.

Students and professors stopped him in the hallways to congratulate him on his "incredible achievement."

Dr. Copeland slapped him on the shoulder grinning happily. "Bolotin," he said, "you did it! I knew you would. My boy, you never cease to amaze me." Even though Dr. Copeland was one of the most supportive faculty members for the students, his praise kept Jacob floating on air for days.

In spite of the mountain of difficulties that confronted him, the study of medicine filled Jacob with such joy it both sustained him and gave him strength.

While laboratory work was an impossibility for him, he loved being in the lab and faithfully attended chemical, bacteriological, pathological, and histological sessions, felt the apparatus, smelled the substances used, made whatever experiments he could, and with his intense concentration, memorized word for word the lectures accompanying them.

Anatomy, which used dissection, was easier, for it enabled him to use his keen sense of touch. He worked with another student and friend, Herman Woehlck, who performed the dissection and read aloud from the text. Then Jacob would "see" the dissected portion with his hands and explore its body location. Though he gained as much practical knowledge in this subject as any sighted student, he was still dissatisfied.

Where his classmates could see the dissected portion and its location in the body, "seeing" it with his hands was not enough for him. He had to find a better way to master anatomy. Time was short. Mid-term exams were four weeks away and Dr. Winnan, the head of the Anatomy department, was known for giving difficult test.

Distraught, he mentioned the problem to Professor Bamberger, who had remained his close friend and advisor since his return from the Illinois School for the Blind. Within hours, Bamberger sent word for Jacob to come to his office. "I think I have the solution," he told Jacob. "I remember your mother telling me, when you and Fred were small she would give you pieces of dough to play with whenever she baked bread. You would mold copies of things around you—a spoon, a fork, a cup. You even tried to duplicate your shoe and Sarah's doll. We have a lot of clay here for our first graders. You can have all you want."

Clay! That was it! If he could find a place for a table in the Anatomy Lab...

"Of course," Associate Professor Bruce Moss assured him. "There's a sort of a catch-all closet along the back wall."

"Yes, sir, I know where that is."

"You're welcome to use it, but it's very cramped, very dusty and dark"

Jacob smiled. "I don't mind the dust, and as for the dark..." They both burst into laughter.

Moss patted Jacob's arm. "It's all yours, Bolotin," he said. "Dr. Winnan won't mind."

There was just enough space for a small table and chair. Jacob spent hours after classes fashioning detailed models of internal parts of the body and arranging them in their proper order. Soon he became as adept as any sighted student at locating any part of the body and could easily identify every organ or muscle given him. At the midterm exam, he received an A.

Entering the classroom the next morning, a classmate accosted him at the door.

"Just a minute, Bolotin."

"Good morning, Lamar." Jacob knew the tense, nervous voice well.

"I just read the grades Winnan posted. How in hell did you get an A?"

"I don't understand you, Lamar."

"You know damn well what I mean! There's no way, no goddamned way you could get an A. Most of us got B's and C's. And we're not blind!"

Jacob let loose the hot anger surging through him. "I may be blind, but I have hands and brains, and I identified every part he gave me!"

"Don't give me that crap! Winnan threw the book at the rest of us. Tried his damnedest to confuse us, but not you. Oh no! You get special treatment. You're a pain in the ass!"

By now the entire class was aware of the fracas and started defending Jacob.

"Lamar! You're the pain in the ass!"

"What's the matter? Sour grapes, Lamar?"

"He earned his A fair and square."

"Like hell he did," Lamar was breathing heavily. "Winnan gives him special treatment. That's why he got that A!"

"You're wrong, Lamar."

Startled, the student swung around. Dr. Winnan was standing directly behind him. His words were sharp and precise. "Everyone was given the same organs in exactly the identical sequence. Every wrong identification cost five grade points. You made five errors. You got a C. Bolotin made none. He got an A."

"But he's blind!" Fury contorted Lamar's face. "He had to make more mistakes than any of us."

"I'll say it again," Winnan's voice was steely cold. "Bolotin made no errors, he got an A. When you make no errors, you'll get an A. Now, do you still accuse me of favoritism?"

A breathless silence blanketed the room. The students watched, riveted, as Lamar glared at the professor, his jaw set, his fists clenched. Winnan didn't move.

Slowly, Lamar seemed to shrink into himself. His body sagged. His head drooped. "No," he muttered through compressed teeth. "I guess not. But," he lashed out defensively, "he'll never be a real doctor. He has no right to be here."

The class bell noisily clattered its warning. No one moved. When its last echoes died away, Winnan replied icily, "Bolotin paid his tuition. He has as much right here as anyone else. And, as for being a real doctor, if he earns his degree, he'll be a real doctor. Now, gentlemen, if you'll take your seats, we'll get on with our class."

The next day Lamar led a delegation of six students to the Chancellor's office demanding Jacob's expulsion from the university.

"On what grounds?" the Chancellor asked. "Mr. Bolotin is making top grades. He has caused no trouble. His tuition is paid promptly. On what grounds shall we expel him?"

"For three reasons," Lamar replied, cockily certain of victory. "First, a blind man can never become a doctor. Second, a blind man trying to study medicine makes a mockery of our profession. Third, he's a Jew!"

"I see," the Chancellor paused and the students shifted nervously from foot to foot. "Before I answer your three charges, I need to know what grades you are making." He scanned the semi-circle of embarrassed faces. "Any of you make A's?" No one answered. "B's?"

One hand rose slowly, "B minus, sir."

"Any C's?" Four hands rose reluctantly. "And you?" He turned to the sixth.

The student squirmed under the Chancellor's level gaze. "D, sir," he whispered.

"Thank you, gentlemen. Now I will answer your three charges. First, a very successful blind doctor is practicing in Chicago today. If you find a blind man challenging, then rise to the challenge instead of wallowing in jealousy and self-pity. Second, Bolotin's teachers say he is one of their best students. He is an asset, not a mockery, to the study of medicine. As for number three, a patient is concerned with his physician's expertise, not his religion. It does not matter whether he is Catholic, Protestant, Jewish or Buddhist. It's ability, not ethnic background, that's important. I suggest, gentlemen, that you lay aside your prejudice and apply yourselves more zealously to your studies. Your request is denied. Good day."

It came as a shock to Jacob that sighted classmates could resent him.

"Why?" he asked Herman. "Why would they begrudge a blind man a chance to make something of himself?"

"Because," Herman explained sourly, "is because you're blind."

"For God's sake, Herm, talk sense."

"Is sense I'm talking—you're not listening. They resent because you give competition."

"That's crazy, Herm! You're talking sheer idiocy. They've got eyes that see, that can read, that can study. They can see the world. They know what a tree looks like. They see the difference between night and day. They see people, a sky full of stars. I want to be a doctor, but I'll never know what skin looks like. I can feel blood, but what does it look like? You tell me it's red, what does red look like? You tell me you have blue eyes. You tell me some things are pale or dark or brown or pink. What is pale? What is dark? What does it mean—pink, blue, light, dark? You can describe an eye or an organ or a face to me until doomsday, but I'll still never know what it actually looks like. Dammit, Herm, don't they understand? How in God's name can I compete with those guys?"

"Sure, Jake, they have eyes, but no brains. You have brains without eyes. Yet you make them feel like what they are—dumbkopfs!"

Within a week after Lamar's outburst, one found his revenge.

When Jacob went, as usual, to his corner of the lab to work at his clay table, his shoes crunched on something scattered over the floor. Reaching down to find the cause, he picked up bits and shards of broken clay. His heart sank as he reached for his models. Every one had been destroyed. Even the clay table lay shattered beyond repair. Jacob never reported the incident.

Only Herman saw how viciously the months of Jacob's painstaking work had been demolished.

"Those stinkin' bastards!" Herman shouted. "I know who did. Lamar! That's who! I'm gonna get him kicked out of school!"

"Herm, I'm as mad as you are, but what's done is done. Nothing will resurrect my models. Besides, I don't want to be the cause of more resentment."

"At least, Jake, we report."

"No, Herm, absolutely not. We just forget the whole thing."

The incident was never mentioned again.

Before the semester ended, three of the malcontents flunked out and left the college. Of the six, only one received his M.D.

CHAPTER 16

Herman brought the news. "On you," he announced, struggling to keep the laughter out of his voice, "many fellas making bets."

"Bets? On me?" Jacob was dumbfounded.

"Yah! Bets!" Herman chortled gleefully. "On you, bet big money."

"All right, Herm, when you get through laughing, will you tell me what the devil you're talking about?"

"Tomorrow, we bandaging begin, yes?"

"So?"

"So! Some fellas they bet you learn quick and make A like always, but some fellas bet bandaging is for you not possible and you fail."

"Did you bet?"

"You betcha! I know Jake Bolotin. I bet whole dollar you make A."

Jacob knew there was only one way he could learn the art of bandaging, how to splint, how to wrap gauze and use adhesive. He had to experience the feel of the bandages on himself. He became "the patient" for his fellow students to practice on. He withstood the ensuing torment which gave him many aches and pains, but he mastered the technique and received an A on the quiz.

Seated in the saloon booth a few nights after the test, a jubilant Herman pressed three dollar bills into Jacob's hand. "Is yours!"

"What's this for?" Jacob asked.

"Is yours! I win from fools six dollars betting you fail." Herman could scarcely contain his elation. "So is three for you and three for me."

Jacob pushed the money away. "Absolutely not. That's your money, not mine."

"No! No! Is yours. The A you make."

"But not because of your bet, Herm."

"No! Because you smart. So!" Herman grinned, "You keep making A, I keep betting on you, and we both get rich."

Only after Herman threatened to stop reading to him did Jacob finally accept the money. For him it was a godsend. Even with the money he'd saved selling typewriters, finances were a perpetual problem. He earned some of his expenses by practicing a bit of Mechano-Therapy but mainly by devoting his weekends, holidays and vacations to selling from his faithful basket of brushes. Each day exhaustion took its toll, but he consoled himself with the promise that "this is the last." He had only one more year before he would be a doctor. Then he could throw the brushes away forever.

Jacob developed a new technique for selling in the exclusive Chicago suburbs. Einar Camfield, another medical student who had become a close friend, accompanied him on these selling expeditions. Their pitch was simple. Ringing the bell of a home, Einar launched into a prepared speech that informed the occupant Jacob was a blind medical student working his way through college. Certainly the resident could use some new toothbrushes or hairbrushes and, at the same time, enable the student to continue his schooling. Einar was tall, ruggedly handsome and very convincing. Some responded with purchases, but fairly often people would look skeptically at the eyes that appeared perfectly normal and launch into an angry tirade. The two friends had, long ago, memorized all its variations.

"What do you take me for—an idiot? That fellow can see as well as I can. Get lost!"

"You've got a damned lot of nerve trying to make me believe he's blind. Tell him to get a decent job and stop pestering people."

"If he's really blind, he'll never be a doctor. If he isn't, you're a coupla liars and you won't get a cent from me."

Their weekend earnings were disappointingly low. Einar was discouraged.

"It's not worth the carfare out here."

Jacob agreed. "But," he said, "let's try once more. Just one more Sunday."

That decision, Einar always admitted, was providential. The man who answered the bell at the first home that Sunday looked quizzically at Jacob. He waited politely until Einar had finished his monologue.

"Young man," he replied, "it doesn't matter if your friend is blind or not. Please let me see his canvassing permit"

"Permit?" Einar echoed. "He needs a permit?"

"I've never needed one before," Jacob replied, struggling to mask his alarm.

The man smiled at the distraught young salesman. "You fellows must be from Chicago. You don't need one there. But you'll find all the suburbs require business permits, and we consider door-to-door selling a business."

"Is a permit expensive?" Jacob asked, steeling himself for the answer.

"No. It doesn't cost a thing. Look, guys, I'm sorry to do this to you. But, if you continue without one, it could cost you a hefty fine."

"A fine!" Jacob was appalled.

"Right. Come back with your permit, and I'll be glad to buy some of those nice looking brushes."

But it was not that easy. Officious suburban bureaucrats refused to believe Jacob was blind and denied him the necessary permits. Word of his problem reached several of his professors who quietly paid a call upon Carter H. Harrison, Mayor of Chicago. A few days later, a startled Jacob received a letter on official "City of Chicago" stationery.

To Whom It May Concern:

Mr. Jacob Bolotin is a student of the Chicago College of Medicine and Surgery and because of his affliction — total blindness — he is compelled to make a living selling toothbrushes from one town to another.

He has had considerable trouble, occasioned by the
fact that his eyes are open, giving rise to the suspicion
that he is not totally blind. His professors inform me
that he has absolutely no sight and that he is worthy of
any consideration in the way of free permits, etc. that
may be given him.

Carter H. Harrison
Mayor

Armed with this letter, permits were granted and sales increased.

A number of magazines and newspapers had written articles about Jacob. These stories caught the attention of Harry Lee Taft, an executive of the Pearsons-Taft Land Bank Credit Company located in Chicago's downtown commercial center. He wrote a letter offering to aid Jacob in any way he could and mentioned his eagerness to meet the young man.

Jacob was deeply moved by the letter. A few days later, he presented himself to Mr. Taft. Their rapport was instantaneous. The handshakes were scarcely ended when Taft offered him a loan to ease his financial problems. Jacob was amazed.

"But you don't know me, Mr. Taft," Jacob replied, struggling to keep his voice calm.

Taft smiled. "I'm known in the business world as an excellent judge of character. I'd consider it a privilege to be of assistance."

Jacob fumbled with his hat. "Mr. Taft," his words were barely audible, "no one has ever offered me such kindness. I'm deeply grateful, but I cannot accept it."

Taft was taken aback. "Why? Why not, Mr. Bolotin? You need the money, don't you?"

"Yes sir, I do. And please, sir, my name is Jacob."

"Good, thank you, Jacob. Now then, tell me what's the problem? Repayment? If that's what you're worried about, I'm in no hurry. Take as long as you like."

"Thank you, sir," Jacob chose his words carefully, "but a debt would be a constant source of worry to me. It will be years before I'll be able to return the loan. I'd feel more secure beginning my professional life free of debts."

Taft nodded. "I understand. And I respect your decision. However, my offer to help still stands. If I can be of assistance in any way, you have only to ask."

Taft kept a close watch upon the young student and occasionally wrote to his teachers to keep track of his progress. Though they became good friends and Taft made many offers of financial assistance, Jacob never asked the banker for money.

But the need was perpetual.

CHAPTER 17

Howard Thurston, billed as "The World's Greatest Magician," brought his act to Chicago and created a sensation. Among the entranced spectators sat Jacob's friend and classmate, Herman Woehlck. For days afterward, he spoke of nothing else. He regaled his listeners with wondrous stories — a woman sawed in half and rising whole from the table; a hypnotized girl floating in air; a plaster statue constructed before his eyes that came to life; a blindfolded mind reader identifying every object his assistant was given by people in the audience.

His enthusiasm amused Jacob, but magic was a realm no blind man could enter. Jacob put it out of his mind. So it was strange that, in the middle of the night, he suddenly sat straight up in bed, awakened by a startling idea that just came to him. If a man, blindfolded, could identify objects, he could do it too. His excitement mounted. He would become a mind reader! Tomorrow he would present the plan to Woehlck. Ideas tumbled on ideas until exhaustion took over and he drifted off to sleep.

When he told Woehlck and Einar Camfield his idea, Woehlick hooted with derision. "Craziest thing I've ever heard. You're too smart for such lunatic ideas."

Jacob was miffed. "Why?" he demanded. "Why is it a lunatic idea?"

"For a dozen reasons. First, we're not mind readers. We're just a couple of med students working our butts off to become doctors. What do you want to do — throw away all our years of school and become actors?"

"Now you're being ridiculous," Jacob retorted. "Of course not. But it would be an easy way to earn some money until we graduate. At least," he added wistfully, "a helluva lot easier than peddling brushes."

Woehlck began to soften, but he was still dubious. "If you think I know how it's done, forget it. I haven't the faintest clue."

"That's it, Herm! You said it! Clues! It's a trick," Jacob persisted. "We know it's a trick. Thurston's a magician, not a psychic or he wouldn't need an assistant. That guy gives him the clues, Herm! We can make up our own clues!"

Camfield thought it might be possible but Woehlck was unconvinced. "You make it sound easy, but we're amateurs. That act was smooth as butter. Must take years to be that good."

"We can do it, Herm. I know we can. We'll work out a code, we'll practice and it won't take years."

"Better not!" Woehlck grumbled. "We haven't even got months."

They practiced in the college basement and were ready in three weeks. Jacob would be the mind-reader and Woehlck the assistant. A trial performance at the saloon was greeted with awed respect and enthusiastic pounding of tables.

Einar was delegated to obtain bookings. With his air of quiet, solid authority, it took only one afternoon to come up with a contract for three weekend bookings.

On opening night, the theatre experienced a sudden boom in ticket sales as a sizeable group of faculty members, led by Dr. Copeland, and a large contingent of senior med students came to cheer on two of their most popular classmates.

As the curtain opened, Jacob was revealed enthroned center stage. He wore a voluminous red velvet robe, lavishly trimmed with wide, jewel encrusted gold brocade. Around his neck hung a gold-fringed collar bearing the signs of the zodiac, and he had a towering purple turban on his head. The exotic costume left no doubt that he was indeed, as billed, "The World's Greatest Swami."

Herman Woehlck stood respectfully beside him, his gaze properly brooding and mysterious. Dressed in a heavily embroidered green tunic tied with a wide gold satin sash, a golden turban and gold satin trousers tucked into high black boots, he was the perfect servant for so great a master.

The lights dimmed and a spotlight focused upon the seated Swami. Of course, unable to see the spotlight, Woehlck whispered to him, "Now!" Jacob placed his hands together in prayer fashion and bowed low. Then, regally erect, with his hands resting on the arms of his throne, in a voice vibrant and deep, he intoned, "I am the Great Swami."

He turned his head slowly from side to side, making certain every member in the audience saw his large, wide open eyes.

"Cosmic spirits," he continued, "have endowed me with the psychic power to read your minds. Soon my servant will pass among you. Those who wish may give him an object of your choice. He will hold it in his hand. He will concentrate upon it and send his thoughts to me. There must be absolute silence so that I may receive his thoughts and identify the object he holds."

He clapped his hands sharply and Woehlck stepped forward.

"I am ready," he announced. "Begin!"

"Yes, Master," Woehlck responded. With hands held prayer fashion, he bowed before the Swami, turned and approached the footlights.

"Ladies and Gentlemen," he began slowly, with all the solemnity and dignity he could muster. "The Great Swami wishes to be blindfolded so that you will know he sees the objects you give me not with his eyes but with his mind's eye. He requests that two volunteers from the audience come forward to apply the blindfolds. Will two volunteers please come to the stage?"

Two men immediately walked down the side and climbed the steps to the stage. Woehlck led them to a small table.

"Gentlemen," he said, "two blindfolds, one white and one black, lay before you. Please examine them carefully."

The volunteers, awkward and self-conscious, placed them around their eyes. "Can you see through them?" Woehlck asked. The men shook their heads. "No," they grinned, "nothing."

Woehlck was relentless. "You must make certain. Test them again. Are you able to look through them?"

The men agreed they saw absolutely nothing.

"Good. Thank you gentlemen," Woehlck said. "Now please take these two large balls of cotton from the table, place one on each eye of The Great Swami. Hold them in place by tying the

white blindfold around him. Then, to make doubly sure he can
see nothing, tie the black one around the white one."

The men obeyed. When The Great Swami had been properly blindfolded and the audience assured he could see nothing,
the two volunteers, grinning, returned to their seats.

Woehlck turned to Jacob, "Oh, Great Swami, are you comfortable?"

"Yes."

"Master, are you ready to begin?"

"I am ready."

Woehlck, followed by a spotlight, began walking up and
down the aisles selecting articles thrust at him by eager members of the audience. He held each one ceremoniously high
above his head and intoned reverently, "Oh, Great Swami, you
to whom all mysteries are revealed, what is this object that I
hold?" Coded clues were, of course, verbally given with each
article.

Catching the key words, Jacob would lift his hands prayer-
fully to his forehead, go into intense concentration, and then
make his Olympian pronouncement.

"I see something round — small — perhaps a ring. No! No!
It's a watch! I see it clearly now. It's a man's gold watch!"

By the time Woehlck returned to the stage and the curtain
fell, hands clutching objects were waving all over the theater as
people clamored for more. Within weeks, other theaters discovered The Great Swami, and Einar Camfield had his choice of
bookings all over the city.

All went well until one ill-fated night when a man offered
a strange object for identification. Woehlck stared in consternation at the tiny cylinder in his hand. A Catholic, he did not recognize a Mezuzah, a small metal tube containing a Hebrew
prayer printed upon a miniature scroll. He stood speechless,
unable to offer any clues. All eyes focused upon Jacob as the
audience awaited the Great Swami's identification. But the
Great Swami was wondering what the devil was wrong with
Woehlck as he felt the long and ominous silence creeping like a
fog across the footlights.

Puzzled, he called out, "My faithful one, do you hold an object?"

"Yes, Great Swami, I do, indeed, hold an object, a strange object," Woehlck's voice warned Jacob. Quickly he flung his hands heavenward and intoned solemnly, "Good and noble friends! My path, the true path of mystery leading my inner consciousness wavers...I am troubled..."

"You bet he's troubled!" screamed the irate theater patron springing to his feet. "He's in bad trouble because they're not mind readers! They're a pair of crooks! The act's a fake! A great big fake!"

Angry voices erupted as the theatergoers took sides, and Jacob realized he had only minutes to save the act and the salary so crucial to their careers. He rose from his throne with a majesty he fervently hoped properly awe-inspiring.

"Hear me!" he thundered. The hubbub stopped abruptly. "I am The Great Swami! My mind's inner eye reads only thoughts that exist in another's mind. I cannot read thoughts that do not exist. My faithful servant, do you recognize the object you hold?"

"Forgive me, Master. It is strange to me. I do not know it."

"Then your mind can convey nothing, and where there is nothing I can read nothing. Return the strange object and find another you recognize so that you can concentrate and send out your thoughts to me. And I must have silence! Absolute silence!"

Suppressing a grin, Woehlck returned the Mezuzah to its disgruntled owner who, by now thoroughly tricked, slunk into his seat muttering to himself. Woehlck selected a child's cap from the many objects thrust at him. Catching their two code words for child and cap, Jacob identified it easily and with great ado. The frenzied applause that followed saved the day.

The act continued and proved so successful the two men often amused their friends by earnestly debating whether they should become vaudevillians instead of doctors.

CHAPTER 18

During the last half of their senior year, the highest ambition of a graduating student was to secure internship at the renowned Frances Willard Hospital. Appointments were won as the result of competitive exams, evidence of superior scholarship and general attainment. Out of nearly 300 graduates, only four were selected. Jacob was one of the four and the only one given the privilege of dividing his time between Willard Hospital and Chicago's Municipal Tuberculosis Dispensaries.

He had never been happier in his entire life. The cadavers, the charts, the skeletons, the textbook cases all lay behind him. At last he was "doctoring" live, breathing men and women. The endless variety of ills that flooded the clinic were a banquet that enriched his knowledge and honed his diagnostic skills. He reveled in the challenges each day brought.

His professors and supervisors agreed the accuracy of his diagnoses were exceptional. His fellow seniors regarded him with awe. They could not understand how, using only his fingers, he could detect minute changes in skin texture, tenseness of muscles, and exactly pinpoint the patients' problems.

He and Herman had a good laugh the day several students challenged Jacob to examine a man with severe chest pain by using only his hands. Jacob bent over the patient and by carefully, slowly palpating his chest found the area of muscle spasm in the intercostal spaces in the right upper lobe of the lung. He described the specific type of lung lesion present. Checking him with their stethoscope, the men found Jacob was right on target.

"I know how he does it," one announced authoritatively. "He's psychic!"

"If I was psychic," Jacob laughed, "I wouldn't have needed four years of med school."

Still, it remained for one case to prove his uncanny accuracy was neither psychic nor accidental.

A frail girl of seventeen with a long history of digestive problems, weakness and increasing shortness of breath was brought to the clinic in a highly distraught state. Her private physician reported she was undergoing severe emotional trauma following the accidental death of her fiancé. Since after repeated examinations he could find no organic cause for her illness, he concluded it was a classic case of neurasthenia [meaning it was a psychological problem].

Careful examination by three of Jacob's fellow students again found no physical malfunction and confirmed the diagnosis of neurasthenia. Accepting their conclusion, when Jacob examined the girl he was stunned to hear the distinct murmur of an obstructed heart valve. Could he be wrong? Slowly he ran his fingers over her chest. Her skin was sweaty and clammy. Again he pressed his ear to her heart and listened intently. There was no doubt. It was not simple neurasthenia, but the dull unmistakable murmur of mitral stenosis. Alarmed, he hurried to the office of his immediate supervisor, Dr. Maxmillian Kuznik, Professor of Clinical Diagnosis.

"Dr. Kuznik," he struggled to keep his voice professionally calm." I hear a diastolic rumble at the apex of the heart and feel a thrill in the same area. The patient, sir, is in heart failure."

Kuznik laughed. "Bolotin," he said, "I'm surprised at you. You're jumping to conclusions. Just because she's having trouble breathing doesn't mean she's in heart failure. Three students have examined her and agree with her doctor, who incidentally is a friend of mine. He's a good man, one of the best."

"They are wrong, all of them. She is in heart failure!"

"I'm sure you realize," Kuznik's voice crackled with ice, "that you are challenging the judgment of an experienced, respected physician?"

Jacob was silent. He knew his fingers and ears had told the truth. Yet Kuznik was warning him. It was stupid and arrogant of a lowly med student to contest the diagnosis of an established physician. He stood mute and miserable.

"You realize that, don't you?" Kuznik repeated harshly.

Everything in him urged Jacob to ask Kuznik to forget the

whole confrontation and walk away. But he could not abandon a critically ill patient. Doggedly he stood his ground.

"I know what I heard," he said flatly. "I believe what I heard, sir," he sputtered in a flash of hot anger. "This girl is dying because of a misdiagnosis!"

"Be careful, Bolotin!"

Jacob was frantic. "Dr. Kuznik, please! Please! Examine her yourself."

"You are sure of your diagnosis?"

"Yes, sir."

For a long moment, Kuznik studied Jacob's tortured face. "Well," he said finally, "I'll give you this, if it was any other student, I'd report him to Dr. Copeland. But with your record — dammit, let's go."

They found a nurse standing beside the girl trying to quiet her. Relieved, she stepped aside and whispered, "Doctor, I'm glad you're here." As Kuznik bent to examine the patient, Jacob stood tensely, listening to the girl's labored breathing.

Minutes ticked by. My God! What was taking Kuznik so long? Couldn't he hear what was so instantly obvious? At last the doctor removed the stethoscope from his ears and gave the nurse a terse order. "Give this patient four 1½ grain tablets of digitalis. Now! And get her to X-ray as fast as possible!"

"Bolotin," Kuznik said as they hurried down the corridor, "Dr. Copeland will receive a full report. A very full report."

The X-ray revealed severe heart blockage. Jacob hoped it had been diagnosed in time to save the girl.

Two days later Jacob was summoned to Copeland's office. The call puzzled Jacob and alarmed Friedman.

"What did you do now?" he chided.

"I don't know!" Jacob muttered as he rushed past him.

When the familiar tapping of Jacob's cane stopped outside the professor's office, he called, "Come in, Bolotin. Come in. Sit down. The 'hot seat' is straight ahead three paces."

Copeland joined happily in Jacob's embarrassed laugh at the revelation that the professor knew what the students naively believed was their secret name for the armchair facing his desk. As the faculty advisor to the senior medical students, it was his job to keep them on track.

"Well," he said, "let's face it, Bolotin. It's pretty hard keeping secrets from your profs."

Abruptly his laughter ceased and Jacob heard the thud of the doctor's body as he sank into his leather swivel chair. Jacob loved this caring, compassionate man and quintessential teacher whose love for "his boys" had earned him the highest accolade the students could give, the title "Pop Copeland." Had he done anything to displease him? Jacob's mind raced through the gamut of possibilities.

Copeland sensed his uneasiness.

"Relax, Bolotin. I just want you to know the patient that was in heart failure two days ago is still critical. But we think she will pull through. If she does, it will be because of your diagnosis. Dr. Kuznik ordered digitalis and X-ray based solely upon your stubborn insistence of valve blockage. He admitted that even with his stethoscope he heard nothing."

"It was very faint, sir, very subtle."

"Still, your ears caught what the stethoscope didn't. Her doctor checked the X-rays and couldn't believe them. You've taught us all a good lesson, my boy. Routine stethoscope examinations are useless to those of us with eyesight unless we listen with the ears of a blind man."

He paused, then sighed deeply. "How arrogant we sighted people are. We were so certain no blind person could achieve anything, least of all medicine. You have proven how wrong we were. Your grade average ranks among the highest we've had in years. You have kept pace with our best students in every phase of medicine, except, of course, surgery."

Jacob heard his teacher's soft, amused chuckle. "You know, Bolotin," Copeland continued, "what is really so fascinating? I think it is actually your lack of sight that has given you the extraordinary sensitivity of touch and hearing that enables you to surpass fellow students in heart and lung medicine. Have you considered specializing in that field?"

"Yes, I have sir, but later on. I think I need years of general practice first."

"I agree. That's very wise, Bolotin. But there is something else I want to talk to you about. You see, there is a reason why you're on the hot seat."

Copeland was silent for a long moment. When he spoke again he made no effort to hide his affection for his blind student.

"Bolotin," he began slowly, searching for the right words. "Building a practice will be harder for you than for any of our boys. To be successful you must win the respect and confidence of your medical colleagues. Without their goodwill and cooperation, you will fail. Dammit!" He banged his fist on the desk. "What I'm trying to tell you is, never, never confront a doctor like you did Kuznik. It seems you were pretty feisty about contesting not only Kuznik's diagnosis but also the diagnosis of her own doctor, who happens to be one of the best in town."

Jacob sank back in his chair, his fists clenched with misery. "But it was wrong, sir."

"Yes, it was wrong. But you should have been less defiant." Copeland's voice softened. "Bolotin, there are gentler ways, more discreet ways of doing that."

"But, sir," Jacob spoke so softly Copeland leaned over to catch his words, "the patient was in heart failure. There wasn't time to be discreet. What should I have done, sir?"

"It was the way you did it—your anger, your bullheaded certainty—and in front of the nurse and other students. That flew right in the face of the eleventh commandment of our profession, which I'm sure you've learned by now."

Embarrassed and ashamed, Jacob mumbled, "Yes, sir. You've told us many times: 'Thou shalt not speak evil of nor dispute the judgment of a medical colleague...,'" Jacob stopped abruptly.

"Go on, finish it, Bolotin, 'in public.' That's the trick—in public. Of course, that doesn't mean you can't differ. What worries me is that with your amazing accuracy, and stubborn honesty, you'll face far more disputes than the average doctor."

"Then what should I do, sir, when the need arises?"

"Tread lightly, my boy. Always remember every doctor's ego is a fragile thing. Tread lightly, respectfully."

"I didn't mean to be disrespectful, sir. My only thought was of a patient who was dying."

Copeland leaned across the desk and grasped Jacob's hand. "You know, Bolotin," he chuckled again, "damned if I wouldn't have done the same thing myself."

CHAPTER 19

On graduation day, May 20, 1912, the university's auditorium buzzed with the excited voices of proud parents. Among them sat Louis and Faga Bolotin. Louis was wearing his best suit, and Faga looked radiant in the new dress she had made for the occasion and a hat borrowed from the landlady. Fred and the other Bolotin children were with them Somewhere in the huge audience sat Jacob's friends, Mr. Taft and Mr. Bennett.

The graduates marched in, self-conscious in their caps and gowns, and took their seats appointed in rehearsal. Jacob had been thoughtfully placed at the end of his row. As they listened to the many speeches, Jacob sat relaxed and happy. For once he didn't have to memorize every word or transcribe it with his Braille stylus. One by one, each graduate walked to the stage to receive his diploma. When Jacob's turn came he carefully counted the twelve steps to the stage, a sharp turn right, two steps, five stairs, left turn and straight forward exactly eight steps to center stage. The university president stood waiting. In a voice that rang through the hall, he announced Jacob's name. As the trembling young man felt the precious diploma pressed firmly into his hand, his fellow students sprang to their feet cheering lustily. Behind them, the entire faculty rose to its feet and prolonged applause swept the hall. Though Jacob would experience many triumphs, the surprise and sweetness of that moment would never be equaled. The dream he had almost denied himself was a reality.

Triumphantly he made his way through the crush of jubilant new doctors, down the familiar corridor to the registrar's office. He stood for a long moment, his hand on the doorknob, remembering the frightened boy, with his basket of brushes, who had stood there four long years ago.

He opened the door and entered the room. Clutton rushed to greet him.

"Congratulations, Bolotin!" he exclaimed, shaking Jacob's hand warmly.

"Dr. Clutton," Jacob said, "I kept my promise. I never came to you with a single request."

Clutton found it difficult to speak. "No, you did not," he replied slowly, his words glazed with guilt. "You certainly did not" He paused. "We want you to know we are mighty proud of you, Doctor Bolotin."

From that day on, neither family nor close friends ever again called him Jacob. His name was now "Doctor." Jacob was the boy who had dreamed and fought for a place in society. "Doctor" was the man who had achieved it.

One hour after his graduation, the new doctor mailed a commencement program, with his name encircled in red ink, via special delivery, to Dr. Robert Babcock.

Doctor Copeland presented him with a stethoscope. "You don't really need this, Jake," he said. "Your ears are far more sensitive than this instrument but wear it anyway. It adds a nice touch of professionalism and will always impress your patients."

Only one obstacle remained. To obtain the required license to practice medicine in Illinois, it was necessary to pass a rigid examination by the State Board of Health. Jacob did not fear the examination. He had passed the toughest exams at school with top grades and had graduated with an outstanding grade average. The worst, he was certain, was over.

Then a completely unexpected blow fell.

The first day applications became available, Jacob, Friedman and Woehlck met in the building lobby to apply for the examination permit. They were directed to the office of Dr. James A. Egan, Secretary and Executive Officer of the Board of Health.

The short, bespectacled clerk at Egan's outer office smiled in greeting. "Good morning, gentlemen. May I help you?"

"We're here to pick up applications for the State Board Medical Exam," Woehlck explained, then added with a nervous grin, "Tell us, is the exam really as tough as we've heard?"

"Yes, it's tough," the clerk replied, "but if you know your medicine you have nothing to fear. Here are your applications," he said handing the papers to Woehlck and Friedman. His manner changed abruptly as he turned to Jacob.

"May I have your name, please?" he said stiffly.

Jacob felt a sudden chill. "Why?" he asked. "You didn't ask my friends for their names. Why do you need mine?"

"Because I think you're the blind fellow that just graduated from the Chicago College of Medicine. You are, aren't you?"

"What's that got to do with it?" Friedman demanded testily.

"I can't give him an application."

Jacob's words cut through the startled silence. "Because I am blind?"

"That's it!" the clerk responded eagerly. "That's it! Oh yes! That's precisely the reason. And my orders are not to let you apply."

"Whose orders?" Woehlck shouted angrily.

"Egan's, Dr. Egan's. He warned me not to give..."

"Then I want to talk to Dr. Egan," Jacob interrupted, his calm voice masking the anger boiling within him.

"Call Egan!" Woehlck demanded. "We all want to talk to him."

"Oh, I'm sorry," the clerk chirped, "that's impossible. He's a very busy man, so he ordered me to..."

"And I," Woehlck thundered as his six foot frame loomed above the frightened little clerk, "am ordering you to call Dr. Egan. Now!"

Abruptly, the inner office door was thrown open and Dr. James Egan strode into the room. He scanned the angry faces, the blazing eyes, Jacob's cane and knew this was the confrontation he had anticipated. He smiled at the clerk.

"It's all right, Clarence. I know what the problem is. Gentlemen, I am Dr. Egan, and you," looking directly at Jacob, "are Bolotin. We know your name and we know you're blind."

"Is that a crime?"

Egan ignored Jacob's sarcasm. "No, that was not your doing. But allowing you to practice medicine would be our doing and that would be a crime."

"Is there a law against it?"

"No, Bolotin." Egan's voice was smooth and condescending. "Laws are not needed to prevent the impossible."

"Impossible only in your mind, Dr. Egan. Chicago already has a blind physician."

"You're referring, of course, to Dr. Babcock. Well, fortunately for him, our state board requirements didn't exist in his day. But we have progressed. We've learned the importance of tests to weed out the incompetents."

"Incompetents!" Woehlck's voice dripped venom. "Jacob was one of the best in our class. His grades often topped us all."

Egan smiled smugly. "Gentlemen, please, let's be reasonable. You and I know that one can excel in medical school yet be a failure as a physician. Mr. Bolotin," he emphasized the mister, "I'm sorry you wasted four years of your life preparing for the wrong profession. There's no possible way you can practice medicine."

"At least," Friedman raged, "let him take the exam."

"I'm sorry, the State cannot allow a blind man to take the examination. Permission is denied."

The news reached Dr. Clutton. Furious, he mobilized Jacob's professors who stormed the State Board of Health offices and demanded the unjust decision be cancelled. After prolonged deliberation, the Board finally withdrew its objections. Jacob would be allowed to take the examination only on condition that he would pay for the stenographers assigned by the Board to record his answers as he responded to each question. Jacob agreed.

The examination lasted for three grueling eight-hour days. In the end, he had to answer the questions all over again, orally to the examiners because the stenographers could not decipher their notes. Jacob missed only one question.

An overly exuberant reporter from the <u>Chicago Tribune</u>, assigned to the story wrote:

BLIND MAN MAY USE KNIFE AS A SURGEON

Jacob W. Bolotin Takes State Examination for License as Physician

FINGERS ARE HIS EYES

He Can Do by Sound and Feeling All Others Do By Sight

Surgical operations may be performed by a blind man if Jacob W. Bolotin today succeeds in passing the examination for a physician's license, which he is taking before the State Board of Medical Examiners at the Coliseum. Up to the present, he has passed every test given him, and his examiners believe he will qualify and become the first blind medical practitioner in the State of Illinois.

THINKS IT NOT REMARKABLE

"A blind physician!" exclaimed the young man yesterday after he had finished dictating his answer to the final question of the examination paper. "Well, is there anything so remarkable about it? Because a man has no eyes is it any sign that he hasn't any brains? That is the trouble with the world and the blind man. All the blind man asks is fair play. Give him an equal chance without prejudice and he generally manages to hold his own with his more fortunate colleagues."

Jacob's grade was among the highest ever recorded in the history of the State Board Examination.

To his credit, Dr. Egan took a special interest in Jacob. Proud of his role in permitting the exam, he told the reporters crowding his office, "According to my recollection, he is the first man, totally blind, who has ever taken the State Board examination. I have glanced at the papers and his treatment of the different questions has certainly been masterly."

The license was granted. Jacob was twenty-four years old.

That night, the family held a dual celebration: Fred's successful move into a new and larger janitorial supply shop, and Jacob's triumph as the first and only blind doctor fully licensed to practice medicine.

CHAPTER 20

Dr. Herman Friedman sold his saloon and used the proceeds to open an office. The day he bid his saloon goodbye, Jacob was there to help him celebrate. Beer was on the house. The word had gone out, and by evening all the regulars had gathered to toast "Hermie-the-Doc."

"For he's a jolly good fellow," they sang, banging their beer mugs on the tables.

"Hermie, me boy," shouted peppery, blue-eyed Mike O'Flannerty in a brogue fresh from Killarney, "tis yourself I'm choosin' for me doc. I'm rememberin' Kravitz. The old Polack fell from his truck, he did, and you patched him up good."

"Yeah, yeah!" chimed in the deep bass of Slezak, a burly cement foreman. "And you stitched my kid up when he cracked his head open. You gonna be the doc for me and my family."

"Let's drink to Hermie-the-Doc!" The drunken voices joined in bleery chorus as the mugs crashed down and feet stamped till the windows rattled.

"Thanks, fellas," Herman said. "Is nice—is very nice you make for me the toasts. But now I'm doctor, how about you call me Dr. Friedman?"

"Shit, Hermie! Don't give us none o' that high falutin' crap," retorted Hank Mackin, who hung around the gym down the block and often served as sparring partner for would-be prize fighters. "Just cause you ain't no more Hermie-the-saloon man don't mean you gotta put on the dog. Your still Hermie. Now your Hermie-the-Doc." He waved his mug, "Here's to Hermie-the-Doc!"

The others raised their mugs and shouted, "Another toast! Another toast to Hermie-the-Doc!"

Friedman was embarrassed. He saw Jacob smiling and waving his glass from behind the bar where he had spent an hour drawing beer for the revelers.

110

"You guys forgetting somebody," he shouted above the din. "Jake is now doctor, too. Doctor like me. So!" He picked up a glass and held it out at arm's length. "Now, we toast my friend, Dr. Jake Bolotin!"

There was sudden, total silence. From across the room, Big Bart saw the smile freeze on Jacob's face. The huge six-footer with the fierce eyes and a soft heart rose unsteadily to his feet.

"Right!" The menace in his voice warned the men, "I'm drinkin' to our pal, Dr. Jake!" He glared at his tongue-tied buddies. "Who's drinkin' with me?" No one moved. "Stand up, you bastards, and toast Dr. Jake!"

Jacob heard the great shoving of chairs as the men rose and banged their glasses together.

"We wish you luck, Jake—you bein' blind and all," Slezak blurted out.

"Aye," O'Flannerty joined in. "Aye! Good luck to you, lad. Tis the luck of the Irish this Jewish boy will be needin'."

Eventually the free beer ran out. The merrymakers departed. Jacob and Herman sat for the last time in the rear booth. Immersed in memories, neither was able to speak. Memories of their four years of slogging stubbornly through the punishing work of med school unrolled within them. Completely dependent upon each other, they had forged trust and friendship out of mutual need. They had supplied each other with the strength, encouragement and solid support that enabled them to celebrate this night as doctors. At last, Jacob murmured huskily, "We made it, Herm. We made it!"

Suddenly he began chuckling. "Hey, Herm, remember the time Professor Schmitz called on you to name the female organs? You were so embarrassed you choked on every word. You had the whole class in hysterics!"

"Yah! Even the word, 'gynecology,' I couldn't spit out. And me with five kids, yet. I was dumbkopf!"

"Well, if you're a dumbkopf, you're a damn smart one! Remember all the fellows kicked out every year? And you know three flunked the final and have to take the whole year over. But we made it, Herm. It wasn't easy for either of us, but we made it! If it hadn't been for you, Herm..."

He stopped abruptly as a surge of emotion overcame him. Furious for allowing himself to sink into such sentimentality, he shoved his long empty beer mug aside and slid out of the booth. Within seconds, Friedman's arms were around him. The two friends stood for a moment locked in silent embrace.

"Jake," Friedman said almost inaudibly, "if not I find you..."

Jacob swallowed, smiled and patted Herman on the back. "Well," he exclaimed jovially, "so long, Dr. Friedman."

The spell was broken.

"So long, Dr. Bolotin. In Polish we say, 'May luck find you soon.'"

"You know, Herm, O'Flannerty was right. It is lots o' luck these two Jewish boys will be needin'." He turned and tapped his way around the familiar tables and out of the saloon for the last time.

CHAPTER 21

Dr. Jacob Bolotin stood at the window of his small office listening to the din of traffic below, and wishing that one, just one person from the throngs passing below would knock on his door. It was not that no one knew he was there. Neat lettering on the front of the building and on his door announced:

JACOB W. BOLOTIN, M.D.

MONDAY THROUGH FRIDAY 8 A.M. TO 9 P.M.

Today was the beginning of his second month. During the past thirty-one days, not a single patient had walked through his door. Still he refused to be discouraged. Doctor Copeland had warned his boys repeatedly, "Building a practice challenges every ounce of your endurance, your grit and your perseverance. Remember," he had said, "it takes endless patience to win patients!" Jacob knew even sighted doctors faced the challenge of establishing a reputation of trust and excellence. He knew all too well that for him the task would be gigantic.

Even finding his office had been a humiliating ordeal. Landlords had refused to rent to a blind man, until he found Sven Larsen. A tall, gangly man with a blond mustache, whose curled sides drooped to his chin, he spoke with the distinctive Swedish cadence that fascinated Jacob.

"I will rent to you," Larsen had said bluntly. "But doctor or no doctor, I know you will not be lasting here long. I will not give lease. You want it month-to-month, okay."

The office was cramped and unsatisfactory, not at all what he wanted, but at least he had an office. With the last of his savings he had furnished it with several second-hand chairs, a desk for his Braille typewriter, a cupboard for medical instruments and supplies and a discarded wooden examining table Doctor

Copeland had resurrected from the college basement. He was ready for the patients who never came.

Jacob turned from the window and began pacing restlessly around the room. Suddenly he was startled by a loud, rapid knocking on his door. His heart leaped. A patient! His first patient! He started quickly for the door, then caught himself. No! No! He must appear calm and professional. He sat down at his desk, took a deep breath and called, "Come in."

As the door opened, he caught the unmistakable rustling of long skirts. Women! He rose and walked forward to greet them. "Come in, ladies."

Two fashionably dressed women entered dragging along a tiny girl who was wailing lustily.

A strident treble voice asked, "Dr. BOLO-tin?"

"Yes," Jacob laughed and corrected gently, "I am Dr. BoLAtin."

The treble voice again, harried and tense, "I am Mrs. Fenton, this is my sister, Mrs. Ada Odell. We've come about my daughter, Cassie. She's been complaining of stomach pain since last night." She pushed the sobbing child forward. "Cassie, stop sniveling and say hello to the nice doctor."

The frightened child clung to her mother's leg and buried her face in her mother's voluminous skirt.

"We'd like for you to take a look at her, Doctor."

"It's obvious she's hurting badly," Jacob replied. "If you will remove her clothes, I'll get her on the table for examination."

"No!" Cassie screamed. "No! I won't take my clothes off! I won't! I won't!"

Though she wept and wriggled and fought, she was no match for her determined mother and aunt. Off came dress and panties. With only her petticoat left to hide her nakedness, she broke loose and fled to the far corner of the room. Crossing her arms tightly across her chest, she crouched down on the floor, an outraged little bundle of defiance.

"Cassandra!" Her mother's patience had evaporated. "Stop acting like a silly baby. We're going to get that petticoat off this minute!"

The frantic child saw only one place to hide. Eluding her mother she darted, silent as a kitten, under Jacob's desk and huddled there, crying piteously.

Jacob's heart went out to the child, but for a moment he was panic-stricken. Where did she go?

"Cassandra!" Her mother's voice sent shivers through the child. "Come out from under that desk now! This second!"

Jacob relaxed. He knew what to do. Motioning the women back, he sat down on the floor behind the desk, leaving Cassie no way out. He reached into a drawer and pulled out a small celluloid kewpie doll. His internship at the clinic had taught him the importance of toys for children. Dancing the toy on his knee, he spoke softly—friend to friend.

"Cassie, can you guess this little doll's name? She doesn't like the name I gave her," he said softly, "and do you know why?" The sobs were lessening. "You'll never guess, so I'll tell you why. Because she wants to belong to you." The sobs stopped. "She wants you to name her. She had a tummy ache like you, and she wanted the pain to stop too. So I listened to her tummy with my ears. Can you guess why?"

He smiled to himself as the tremulous answer came, "N-n-no."

"Then I'll show you why." He put his ear upon the tiny doll's stomach. "Her tummy talks to me and tells me why it hurts, and then I know how to make it well. Here, she's your doll now. You listen."

The little girl took the doll and pressed her ear against the kewpie's rounded belly. Jacob waited.

"I don't hear anything."

"That's because my ears are different than yours, and if you'll come close to me so I can whisper, I'll tell you why."

He felt the tiny child cuddle against him. "Cassie," he whispered, "it's because I can't see with my eyes like you can. I'm blind."

"But you're looking right at me."

"But I can't see you, even right here, sitting beside me. When you take your petticoat off, I won't see you either, but my ears will listen to your tummy."

"Will it talk to you?"

"Of course, and it will tell me how to make you well."

"And you really won't see me?"

"No, not even the teensiest bit."

"All right." She ran to her mother. "You can take my petticoat off, Mommy. And please, hold the kewpie doll he gave me."

Mrs. Fenton breathed a sigh of relief. "Good girl, Cassie, now let the nice doctor see what's wrong with you."

Jacob lifted the child onto the table. After examining her with his stethoscope, he placed his ear upon her abdomen.

"Look Mommy!" the child burbled excitedly, "My tummy's talking to the doctor because he can't see me."

"What? Doctor, what is she saying?"

"She took her petticoat off," Jacob replied, "because I told her I am blind."

"It wasn't right to lie to her, Doctor," Mrs. Fenton said indignantly.

"I didn't lie, Mrs. Fenton. I am blind."

"My God!" the woman shrieked, "I thought you were a real doctor!" She raced to the table and grabbed Cassie. "Get off this table, off, this minute!"

"Oh my! Oh my!" Mrs. Odell moaned. "Martha Mae, you let that nasty man put his hands all over that sweet child."

"Well, how did I know he was blind?" Martha Mae snarled as she jammed the clothing on the bewildered child.

"Now, Cassandra!" The little one shuddered, she knew that tone of voice. "What did he do to you behind that desk?"

"He gave me the kewpie doll."

"What else did he do? Tell me everything he did to you."

"He didn't do anything, Mommy."

"He put his hands under your petticoat, didn't he?"

Cassie burst into tears. "No, Mommy. He just talked to me."

Stung by the women's insinuations but concerned for the child, Jacob kept his anger under rigid control. "Madame," he said, "Cassie has appendicitis."

"I don't believe you, not a word you say."

Jacob persisted. "She needs immediate medical attention."

"Well, if she does, it won't be from you. It'll be from a real doctor!"

Jacob could contain himself no longer. "I am a real doctor," he lashed out and pointed to the wall where Louis had hung his diploma and license. "If you will look over there you'll see my M.D. credentials to practice medicine."

"And how many palms did you grease to get these forgeries?"

"Martha Mae!" her sister was worried, "maybe they are real. And besides he didn't hurt Cassie any."

"Are you crazy, Ada? He knows he's a fake! We know he's a fake. And make no mistake, sir, God knows you're a fake!"

Jacob couldn't resist. "And," he asked politely, "may I know what God told you?"

"Oh!" Martha Mae choked, "That's blasphemy! Let's get out of here. And as for the doll...give it to me, Cassie."

"No, Mommy, please," Cassie sobbed, hugging the doll to her heart. "Let me keep her. Please, Mommy."

The mother snatched the doll from the child's hand and hurled it across the room. "That's what I think of your doll, and that's what I think of you!"

As the women stomped out of the office, Martha Mae turned for her final fling. "You should be ashamed of yourself. God will punish you for this."

The door slammed shut and Jacob stood motionless listening to Cassie's wailing and the women's heels clattering away down the long hallway. Then, sick at heart, he knelt and crawled around the room until he found the kewpie doll.

Jacob's long day was not over. That afternoon, Sven Larsen came to collect the rent.

"Well, young doctor, today begins second month. You have yet no patients, yes?"

Jacob laughed. "I have yet no patients, yes."

"I tell people you here, but they say when sick they go to real doctor."

"I am a real doctor, Mr. Larsen. Tell those people I am a real doctor."

"No," Larsen contradicted firmly. "You a blind doctor, not real doctor. You think to last maybe another month?"

"I don't give up that easily, Mr. Larsen," Jacob replied as he handed him the rent he had borrowed from Fred. "I'll be here."

"Okay, I come again next month for rent." Larsen walked to the door and stopped. An honest man, he was genuinely worried about his stubborn tenant. "I think," he said softly, turning back to Jacob, "is wrong to throw out good money. I think you are very foolish young man."

It was a verdict Jacob could not accept, but he was not one to fool himself. "Larsen is right; those women are right," he told Fred later that night as they sipped tea in Faga's kitchen. "Somehow, to survive, I must prove I'm a 'real' doctor."

Fred picked up his half-empty glass of tea and slammed it down on the table. "You know, Doctor," his voice shook with anger, "you're a real shnook! You sit there and worry 'how can I prove I'm a doctor?' You listen to those self-righteous, self-appointed messengers of God! Who the hell anointed them? And as for Larsen, so he owns a building—that gives him brains? I don't remember his name among the biblical prophets. Collecting rent doesn't give him the right to ladle out lousy advice."

Jacob smiled, he was accustomed to his brother's tirades. But Fred wasn't finished.

"Goddamit! You graduated almost at the top of your class. Copeland said you were tops in the clinic. You missed one dumb question in the State Board exam. And now!" He gave his fork a vicious thrust into Faga's apple pudding, "You sit there like a damned idiot and worry how to prove you're a doctor!"

"Fred, calm down!"

"Why? Why should I calm down? I'm sick and tired of these people. They make me vomit. They're all alike. Their moronic brains can't conceive that we may be capable of achieving anything. If we prove we can on Monday morning we have to prove it again Monday night, and Tuesday morning and Tuesday night, and over and over again!"

Jacob listened in stunned silence. Never in all their years together had Fred revealed the depth of his bitterness. Fred's angry words rushed on.

"God ought to make everyone blind for one week, no, one day—just one day. Then maybe an infinitesimal glimmer would penetrate their thick skulls of what we go through every day of our lives. Maybe they'd discover we aren't freaks. We have two good arms and hands and feet and legs! We have heads with mouths and ears and brains. We feel hate and love and hunger and fear just like they do. We bleed just like they do. And now those stinking bastards have got you bleeding—how to prove you're a doctor! Those goddamned sonsabitches!"

Fred stopped as suddenly as he had begun, emotionally drained. "My tea is cold," he said and pushed his glass aside. Jacob remained silent. He understood his brother's need to vent his rage. Fred had never come to terms with his blindness. Yet he had stoically slogged his way through the mire of antipathy and suspicion of the sighted world to become a successful businessman.

The brothers sat silently for several moments,. When Jacob sensed Fred's agitation had passed, he said gently, "Try to understand, Fred. Those women, Sven Larsen, have really done me a favor...a big favor."

"Dammit, Doctor! You make me sick, too!" Fred slumped back wearily in his chair. "Always seeing the best in people. Can't you, for once, see them for the bigoted fools they are?"

"Of course I see it. But, Fred, it's that bigotry that has awakened me to reality. I've been living in a dream. I thought once I opened my office the world would open up like some kind of magic box. But there is no magic box. People with eyes want doctors with eyes. If I sit in my office for a hundred years, patients will never come to me. No, I must go to them. Thank God for Sven Larsen and those women. They taught me my struggle didn't end with a degree or a license. My real struggle is just beginning."

CHAPTER 22

Doctor Copeland stared in surprise at the figure standing in his office doorway.

"Bolotin! Come in! Come in! It's good to see you. Here," he took Jacob's arm, "please sit down."

"In the hot seat, sir?"

Copeland's laughter filled the room. "It all depends, Jake," he replied as he seated Jacob. "Do you deserve it?"

"Well sir, if you were to grade me on the number of patients I have, you'd flunk me."

"I see," Copeland murmured almost under his breath. There was a momentary silence, then he pulled up a chair beside Jacob. "Many of us have been wondering how you're doing. It's been rough, hasn't it?"

"I didn't expect it to be easy, sir."

"No, especially not for you."

"Doctor Copeland, I need your help."

"Of course, Jake, whatever I can do."

"Sir, can you arrange for me to go back to work at the Municipal Tuberculosis Clinic? That is, if they would have me back."

"Have you back!" Copeland chuckled gleefully. "This is amazing. You won't believe this, Jake. Just two weeks ago we asked the clinic if they'd like any of our interns back. They said, 'No, only Bolotin. He radiates such sympathy and concern that the patients love him. They're constantly asking for him. He never forgets a patient's name and over half of them don't know he's blind. Is there any possibility we could get him back?' And here you come today asking if they'd allow you to come back. The answer, Jake, is with open arms, my boy, with open arms. But," he hesitated, "there's a problem."

"Problem, sir?"

"A serious one. They are, as usual, short of funds. They can't pay you."

"Would they allow me to continue working as I did during my senior year, as a volunteer?"

"Oh, they'd be delighted, I'm sure. But I won't permit it. Absolutely not. You aren't a student intern anymore. You are a fully licensed professional. You've earned the right to be paid."

"Earning it is not enough, sir. I have to prove I deserve to be paid."

There was a pause. "Bolotin, why the clinic?"

"My empty office taught me that since patients won't come to me, I must go to them. I'm best at heart and lungs. Those are the patients at the clinic. Perhaps there I can prove I'm what people call 'a real doctor' and, eventually, even the right to be paid."

Copeland's words came slowly, "I'll make immediate arrangements for your return."

When Jacob walked into the clinic, he was surprised and deeply touched by the warmth of his reception. During the few hours he was there, every member of the staff made it a point to greet him personally and tell him how much he had been missed. Since Copeland had informed them Jacob would be giving up his own office hours to serve the clinic, it was decided that he would work mornings from 9 o'clock until noon, Monday through Friday. The arrangement pleased Jacob. Though he lost travel time, it still enabled him to spend the rest of the day in his own office. The lettering on his door now announced:

OFFICE HOURS 2 TO 9 P.M.

As days melted into months, his mornings were busy and rewarding with a heavy patient load. His office remained silent and empty. The door opened only once. A man needed emergency bandaging. Receipts for his first six months came to exactly two dollars.

But expenses continued to mount. Office rental, supplies, food, and carfare came to a staggering seventy-five dollars a month. By borrowing from Fred and spending weekends selling with his basket of brushes, just as he had done throughout his school years, he managed to keep his office open. But taking money from Fred was a humiliation that bothered him enormously.

Fred understood. "Doctor, stop worrying," he urged his brother repeatedly. "My business is good. I'm fine. I don't need the money. When you become rich and famous, then we'll settle up."

But Jacob knew it was not as easy for Fred as he pretended. Even though he was discouraged and angry that as a doctor he still needed to sell brushes to make a living, it never occurred to him to concede defeat. Stubbornly optimistic, he assured worried friends, "Only a worm can't fall. I'll get up again. You'll see. My luck will change."

The following Sunday, it did.

CHAPTER 23

A beautiful dawn ushered in that rare Chicago day—crisp, dry, invigorating and totally devoid of the biting winter winds that so often plagued the city.

Jacob always said that for him, the sequence of events that day were little short of uncanny.

The day began as usual for Adolph Van Teslaar. In his warm, steam-heated bathroom, he finished showering and smiled at his reflection in the mirror. It wasn't the handsomest of faces, but it possessed a rugged, honest, attractive masculinity that won friends and, more importantly, patients. He was satisfied. He slicked down his blonde hair and went into the kitchen for his ritual Sunday treat, hot cinnamon rolls and a pot of aromatic Turkish coffee, a yearly Christmas gift from a friend in Istanbul.

It was a feast to be enjoyed leisurely as he read the Sunday morning <u>Tribune</u>. Breakfast was almost finished when he glanced at the clock. Nine-thirty! If he didn't hurry, he'd be late for the 10 o'clock meeting at the club. Grabbing a coat, he reached the corner just as the streetcar was rolling to a stop.

He noticed that a peddler, descending from the rear platform, was having difficulty negotiating with a cane and a large basket of brushes. As the man groped for support, Van Teslaar sprang forward and grasped his arm.

"Here!" he said. "Let me help you. Give me the basket till you get down."

The peddler smiled and replied, "That's okay. I'll manage."

The peddler felt the basket lifted from him and a firm hand guiding him down.

"Hold it a sec, be right back," Van Teslaar called to the conductor. "Hey fella," he said as he led the peddler to the sidewalk and returned the basket, "that's an awfully big load to handle with one hand. Better take care."

The impatient conductor clanged the bell and Van Teslaar leaped aboard. As the streetcar took off he caught a glimpse of the peddler waving his cane in farewell.

Reviewing the incident in his mind, something troubled him. The man's face seemed vaguely familiar. He had seen it before. Suddenly he remembered. Of course! It was the face in the newspaper clipping lying in his drawer. It was the story of a blind doctor who had just received his license to practice medicine. The story had impressed Van Teslaar so much that he had resolved to meet this remarkable young man. But the more he thought about it, the more he concluded it could not have been the same man. This guy was a peddler with two good eyes. He certainly wasn't blind.

He tried to focus upon the club's activities, but the basket man stayed on his mind. The club secretary invited him home for Sunday dinner. For a bachelor, a home-cooked meal was usually irresistible. Instead he found himself murmuring, "Thanks, but not today. Try me again next week," as he yielded to an overwhelming urge to return home.

Unlocking the front door at 1:00 PM, he went straight to his desk and retrieved the clipping from the drawer. The face of the peddler gazed up at him. The back doorbell rang. Still in minor shock, the clipping clutched in his hand, Van Teslaar walked absentmindedly through the kitchen and opened the door. He stared in mute disbelief into the face of Dr. Jacob Bolotin. Little chills ran up his spine until he found his voice and his manners.

"Hello," he said. "May I help you?"

Stunned surprise knotted Jacob's forehead. "Sir," the words came hesitantly, "aren't you the man who helped me off the streetcar?"

"Yes. Yes I am," Van Teslaar replied. "But how did you know that?"

Jacob laughed. "I seldom forget a voice."

"That's incredible! I don't think I said a dozen words."

"It was enough. But you were gone so fast I couldn't thank you. Meeting you again is a real piece of luck. Now I can thank you properly."

Van Teslaar was embarrassed. "Look, it wasn't anything. There's really no need..."

"Yes, there is a need," Jacob interrupted. "You would've had a long wait if you'd have missed that streetcar. Yet you took time to help a blind man."

Uncomfortable, Van Teslaar changed the subject. "Well," he joked, "your basket is certainly much lighter since this morning."

Jacob smiled. "There's still enough to choose from. Please, allow me to express my thanks by selecting whatever you like — a toothbrush, a hair brush, a whisk broom — whatever you wish."

"No, no!" Van Teslaar stammered. "That's most unnecessary."

"Please," Jacob begged. "Please."

There was a pause. Finally, still reluctant, Van Teslaar replied, "Okay, I will accept a toothbrush if you'll permit me to buy the nine you have left. As a dentist I'm always in need of toothbrushes for my patients."

Jacob laughed heartily. "You drive a hard bargain, but okay, it's a deal."

"Good. Please come inside while I get money to pay you. Will you accept a check?"

"From a dentist," Jacob teased, "of course."

Van Teslaar led Jacob to a chair in the kitchen and murmured, "I'll be right back." In a moment, he returned, pressed a check into Jacob's hand and said casually, "I've made it out to you, Dr. Jacob Bolotin."

Utterly dumbfounded, Jacob sat speechless, his face burning with shame.

"That's correct, isn't it?" Van Teslaar asked gently.

"How did you...I don't understand." Jacob struggled for words. "We've never met...how did you...?"

"I think I really knew this morning."

"How?"

"It's very simple. I recognized you from your picture in the papers. I've kept every article written about you."

Jacob shook his head in bewilderment. "Why?"

"Because I wanted to meet you. In fact, I had decided to get in touch with you, probably by next week."

"Why would you want to do that?"

"I've been looking for someone to share my office. I felt you might be the right one, that we could be mutually beneficial. I have a good practice, a large office. I could be of help to you."

"But what can I offer you? I have no money, no patients. What good can I possibly be to you?"

"Can you administer gas anesthetics?"

"Yes."

"Would you be willing to give medical advice whenever it's needed?"

"Of course."

"Would you be willing to answer the telephone in my office?"

"Yes, of course."

"So, you see! You offer me everything I need. It's a perfect partnership. Will you accept?"

It was so sudden. Jacob struggled to believe this was really happening. It couldn't be. "Are you joking?" he asked tensely.

"Of course not. I wouldn't ask if I didn't..."

"You are serious?" Jacob interrupted, his heart pounding. "You really mean it?"

"Yes, Jacob. I really mean it. Will you accept?"

"But, you don't know me. You don't know if I'm honest or dependable or punctual..."

"I know all I need to know from the stories about you. But let's turn it around. What do you know about me?"

The two men burst into laughter and the partnership was sealed.

Jacob notified Sven Larsen he was moving out and the landlord came to say goodbye.

"I know you would not be lasting long," he said, nodding wisely. "Is good you are not throwing out more good money for to be real doctor." He put a comforting hand on Jacob's shoulder, "I know you will find good job, blind man's job. Just don't give up."

The following week, Fred, Einar Camfield and his brother moved Jacob's furniture into Van Teslaar's suite that consisted of a consulting room the dentist had vacated for Jacob, his own impressively equipped dental office, and a nicely furnished waiting room.

Jacob eagerly welcomed Van Teslaar's suggestion that he keep expenses down by sleeping on a cot in his office. When Faga heard of the arrangement, she quickly provided linens and blankets to make certain her son was comfortable. Fearful that he was depriving the family of needed bedding, he accepted them only after Faga assured him, "These yours. For years, I hid them away for your bride. Now you need. So, use in good health, my son. Please God, when you have bride, I will make new ones."

The arrangements were simple and immensely satisfying for Jacob. He took over the task of administering gas anesthetics, sterilized Van Teslaar's instruments, gave medical advice whenever needed, answered the telephone, and cared for the office during Van Teslaar's absence. In return, the dentist answered Jacob's phone when he was away mornings at the Municipal Clinic, read to Jacob and referred patients to him. Soon Jacob's earnings skyrocketed to an average of three dollars a day.

"Almost as much," he told Van Teslaar with a merry grin, "as I made selling brushes door-to-door."

Before long the two men became invaluable assistants to each other and forged a relationship that grew into a lifelong friendship.

At last Jacob's days were filled with satisfying work.

CHAPTER 24

Jacob's patient load at the Chicago Municipal Clinic and Sanitarium increased daily as word spread of his extraordinary thoroughness of examination, his patience, compassion, gentleness and especially his expertise as a diagnostician. Jacob felt increasingly confident that one day soon he would be paid for his work there.

While examining his seventh patient on a very busy morning, Dr. Stewart, the clinic superintendent, sent word for Jacob to come to his office. Puzzled, Jacob told his next patient, "I'll be back in a few minutes," and tapped his way to the superintendent's office.

"You wanted to see me, Dr. Stewart?"

"Yes. Please sit down, Dr. Bolotin."

"Thank you, but I have patients waiting."

"Yes, of course. Then I'll come right to the point. I called you in because I'll be leaving for a meeting before you're through, and there's something you must know." He hesitated, obviously deeply disturbed. Finally, he blurted out, "Please sit down! I don't like to keep you standing. Please, Bolotin, sit down."

"Of course," Jacob murmured. A slight movement of his cane felt the chair beside him. He sat down and waited.

"Look! I'll tell it to you straight! Yesterday I went to see the big shots at City Hall to arrange for you to be paid. I told them it's ridiculous for a doctor of your caliber working for months as a volunteer, that you've earned the right to be paid a thousand times over. I told them I don't want to lose you. But...," he stopped abruptly.

"But, sir?"

Frustrated, Stewart spat the words out. "They said they can't stretch the budget another dollar. Maybe later..."

Jacob suddenly felt very tired. "Maybe later... that could mean years."

"I had to tell you. I'm sorry, Bolotin. Dr. Copeland is furious. He says we're taking advantage of you, and I guess we are. But the truth is, you're one of the best doctors we've ever had, and I hate like hell to lose you."

Suddenly he began to chuckle. "You know what's really funny, Bolotin? The city won't pay you because you're blind. But because your eyes look so normal, half your patients don't even know you're blind. It's ridiculous!" He sighed, "Damn it, I wish to God I could do something about it, but I can't."

While Jacob wasn't surprised, he was angry. It took him a moment to steady his voice before he could reply.

"Thank you for leveling with me, Dr. Stewart. You tried and I appreciate it." He arose and held out his hand. Stewart jumped up to grasp it. "I've enjoyed working here with you and a great group of people, but it's time for me to leave."

"I understand," Stewart tightened his grip on Jacob's hand. "Good luck, Dr. Bolotin. I'm going to miss you, and there's going to be a helluva lot of disappointed patients."

Jacob smiled bitterly. "Not as disappointed as I am."

That afternoon, the trip back to his office downtown seemed interminable. As he opened the door, Van Teslaar rushed to greet him.

"Jake!" he exclaimed. "Dr. Copeland called. There's an opening at the Cook County Tuberculosis Hospital in Dunning. He wants you to apply right away."

Jacob began to laugh.

"What's funny, Jake?"

"The way things happen. I guess it must be true what people say. 'When God closes one door, He opens another.'"

He sent in his application. It took two weeks for the reply to arrive. When the postman handed the mail to Van Teslaar, he whooped with excitement.

"Jake! It's here! It's here! I'll read it to you."

He ripped the envelope open. "I'll bet it's a job. It's gotta be a job."

Jacob sat tensely as Van Teslaar began to read.

"*Dear Sir,*

The Cook County Commission declares your infir-mity makes you incompetent to practice medicine, and has voided your application. "

There was a long, frozen silence as Van Teslaar stood star-ing at the letter in his hand. "The bastards!" he hissed. "The goddamned bastards! Tell them to go to hell, Jake."

Jacob shook his head. His disappointment was raw and sharp. "I wish I could, Van. Oh, God! How I wish I could."

"What do you mean—you wish you could? For God's sake, doctors are sending patients to you, calling you for consultation. Doesn't that mean anything?"

"You know it, and I know it, but evidently the Commission doesn't."

"Then tell them! Goddammit! Tell them. If you don't, I will. I'll raise a stink all the way to Springfield. Springfield? Hell no! To the White House!"

He was pacing up and down the room now, fists clenched, face blazing with anger as he raged on.

"All the way to the White House, that's where! And all that malarkey about being 'created equal.' You're not equal, Jake. You've got an 'Infirmity.' Infirmity! Oh, what a delicate word. Those idiots don't understand it's precisely your 'Infirmity' that makes you a helluva lot better than most of the other doctors. And I'm going to tell them so!"

"Telling them is useless, Van. Meaningless. Don't you see it? All my months of volunteering at the clinic changed nothing. This judgment will plague me as long as I live. I know that, and I've got to stop it. Now!"

"Good! I'll go with you. Together we'll knock some sense into their thick skulls."

"Van! Van! Listen to me—listen! Telling is not enough. I have to prove it to them all over again."

He volunteered to work at the Dunning hospital without pay, an offer eagerly accepted by superintendent, E.V. Cox. For nine months, Jacob came regularly twice a week. Wednesday he was in charge of the tuberculosis ward for the insane at the dispensary in Dunning and every Friday for the inmates in the tuberculosis ward at the Chicago House of Correction.

His heart ached for these unfortunates, and he lavished his love on them as he diagnosed and prescribed treatment with an accuracy that astounded the entire staff.

Harry Lee Taft learned of Jacob's long months of service without salary and his steely determination to prove his competence to the County Commissioners. Enraged at the gross injustice, Taft decided to act. On May 1, 1913, he sent a letter to the president of the board, Alexander A. McCormick, urging him to make a closer, unprejudiced appraisal of the young doctor's qualifications.

On May 8, Taft received a short letter from McCormick in which he wrote:

> *"I had a talk with Doctor Bolotin last Sunday and was very much surprised and impressed with his story. If you have any more men of his caliber lying around, I would like to know of it."*

A few days later, Jacob was appointed attending physician at the county facility. The next morning, Chicago newspaper editors, alerted to the sensational appointment, highlighted the story. The reporter for the Chicago Daily News interviewed Jacob at his home:

BLIND DOCTOR MARVEL; MADE HOSPITAL EXPERT

Jacob W. Bolotin Appointed Attending Physician at Dunning Tuberculosis Branch.

AUTHORITY AT AGE OF 25

Gives Temperatures by Feeling Skin
and Pulse Without
Aid of a Watch.

Dr. Jacob W. Bolotin, a blind physician of Chicago, whose achievements rival those of Helen Keller, yesterday was appointed attending physician of the tuberculosis hospital at Dunning.

Dr. Bolotin is 25 years old and the only blind man who ever has taken a full four-year course in medicine and passed the present Illinois examination for medicine and surgery. He also is licensed to practice osteopathy, massage and medical gymnastics.

LIST OF ACHIEVEMENTS

Here are a few of the wonderful things this young man does:

- Gives exact temperatures of patients by feeling of the skin.
- Gives exact pulse count without use of a watch.
- Diagnoses tuberculosis-infected chests by touch.
- Makes his way all over the city without a guide.
- Has examined over 3,500 patients for the city and county and less than fifty of them know he is blind.

- Uses the touch system in typewriting, yet he cannot write his own name with a pen or pencil.
- Keeps a loose-leaf book as well as any business bookkeeper.

Before the farewell handshake, the interviewer is laughing over funny poetry and funny stories, just as the nurses at Dunning laugh over them every Wednesday, when the blind physician appears. He is a favorite there. They make a special apple pie for him—and he's mighty fond of apple pie—every time he comes.

"Yes, I have just received word of my appointment," said the doctor. "This is my first real success, and I am happy. It has been a long, hard fight. And I want to say this of President McCormick of the county board—he has done in one minute something that will benefit blind people for all time. He has opened another pathway by which the blind may convince the public that they are just as capable as those who see."

Harry Taft was elated at the success of his letter. He waited until September before writing to Superintendent Cox:

"I beg to ask if you will tell me, in strict confidence, just what your opinion of him may be and his qualifications for success."

Cox did not delay his response. During the following few days, he called twice on Taft to speak to him personally. Finding Taft out of the city, he left him a letter.

"I am certainly pleased to have an opportunity to say a good word for Dr. Bolotin. He visited the

Tuberculosis Hospital all last winter through snow and
storm and observing his zeal and being convinced of his
ability, I made up my mind to do anything I could to
help him.

At the first opportunity, I spoke to Mr.
McCormick about him. He had me write him a letter,
and this supplemented by your help and others, he
secured the appointment. I can't say that some of the
MDs were very much pleased at this, but he made good
and is loved and respected by all who have come in con-
tact with him.

Dr. Schroth, who has coached over 6,000 MDs in
anatomy, told me that Bolotin was the brightest in the
6,000 and that he would be willing to match him
against the best on examination of the heart and lungs. "

The appointment carried with it a salary of one hundred
dollars a month and maintenance, if he wished it.

"I preferred to maintain myself and my office," Jacob wrote
years later, "for I realized that my position was political, that I
might be replaced at any time, and that my office was my permanent means of success. I made good in this work and it is
needless to say that, as soon as I received the position, I gave up
selling brushes."

At last, his days of tramping from house to house were
over.

He was finally a doctor full time.

CHAPTER 25

Dunning was a two-hour journey from Jacob's office, and he left before daybreak to be ready for his early morning patients. In the predawn, streetlights blazed like a thousand small suns to light the darkness for the sighted. In his black world, Jacob had no need of the light to find his way.

What Jacob needed were the familiar sounds and medicinal smells of a busy hospital, and he exulted in the endless, exciting challenges each new day brought. He worked in the hospital from eight o'clock in the morning to four in the afternoon, examining twenty or more new patients and making medical rounds twice daily. In addition, he was assigned night duty once a week and for seven weeks was in full charge of the medical department.

Van Teslaar took care of the office during Jacob's absence, answered phone calls and made appointments for him. Back in his office by six o'clock, Jacob saw private patients until nine PM. Soon his combined earnings reached $150 to $175 a month, enough to support his parents and himself in modest comfort without the constant pressures of the past ten years.

Suddenly, early in 1914, Illinois decided to absorb the Dunning County Hospital into the state hospital system and required all employees to submit to re-examination. When Jacob appeared to take his examination, he was surprised to be greeted by reporters. A few days later, Chicago newspapers carried the exultant news.

DR. JACOB W. BOLOTIN PASSES WITH THE HIGHEST GRADE OF ANY ENTRANT

> With a ninety-six point average, he won over fifty competing candidates in spite of the fact that he had to dictate his

answers to a boy of twelve and lost points
because of the boy's errors in spelling and
writing.

He was appointed attending physician at the Tuberculosis
Hospital in Oak Forest. Stories about his "incredible achievement" began appearing in magazines and newspapers across
the country. A reporter from the Philadelphia Inquirer, sent to
interview him wrote:

> "It is one of the most amazing instances of mind tri-
> umphant over physical handicaps that the world has ever
> known... He will rank with Helen Keller as one of the won-
> derful blind persons of history."

Five months after his new appointment, the hospital board
of directors, exceptionally pleased with Jacob's work, asked him
to devote full time to the institution. Instead, he decided to
resign. His private practice had grown rapidly, and new
patients clamored for appointments. "One of the proudest
moments of my life," Jacob recalled, "was when I was able to
resign a state job paying $125 a month, because my private prac-
tice commanded my entire attention."

In addition, he was frequently called in for consultations by
other physicians.

Now that he had achieved professional status and a
respectable income in the two years that had passed since his
graduation, Jacob decided that, at last, he could afford a room of
his own and a more comfortable bed than the folding cot in the
office. He began asking around about rooms he might rent.

His search was brief.

Helen Willens, a petite, attractive, bright young woman
with a keen sense of history and an insatiable curiosity, had
heard about the handsome doctor.

Intrigued, she confided to her sister, Berniece, "I simply
must take a peek at that doctor. It's time for me to see Dr. Van
Teslaar again. I'm sure my teeth must need a cleaning."

Seated in the dentist's chair, she shyly confessed why she had come. Van Teslaar promptly introduced her to Jacob.

"Dr. Bolotin, meet Helen Willens, one of my best patients. Her teeth are in excellent condition. What she wants to see you about, she'll have to tell you herself."

As he left the room grinning happily, Jacob motioned Helen to a chair.

"Miss Willens, please sit down. Now, tell me what's troubling you."

"Well, actually," Helen was embarrassed. "I'm not here because I'm sick." Jacob waited. Finally, she blurted out, "I just wanted to meet you."

It was Jacob's turn to be embarrassed. "Meet me? Why?"

"Well, I read so much about you. I've kept all the stories in the newspapers and magazines about you, and, well, I've always been very curious."

Jacob laughed. "So! Now that your curiosity is satisfied, you must satisfy mine. Since you know all about me, tell me about yourself."

During the happy animated conversation that followed Jacob was captivated by her charm, and Helen knew she had to see more of this astonishing young man. When Jacob asked if she knew of any available rooms, she exclaimed, "We have a room for rent!"

"Good," he responded, and asked if he could come to "see" the room that afternoon.

"Of course!" Helen replied, and rushed home joyously to alert her mother.

It was a Friday and her mother was busy baking the traditional breads and pastries for the Sabbath. When Helen burst into the kitchen, flushed and excited, babbling that a prospective boarder would be there soon, her mother stared at her in confusion.

"Boarder?" she asked. "What are you talking about?"

"He's coming to rent a room!"

"Who is coming? What room? We have no room to rent."

"Yes, we have!" Helen bubbled. "We have one! We do!"

"Where?" her mother demanded angrily. "We are six people in five rooms. Whose room do you want to rent?"

"Mine!" Helen exclaimed. "He can have my room."

A half-hour later Jacob walked the short distance to the Willen's flat. When Helen's mother answered the door, Jacob inhaled the sweet aroma of cinnamon cakes and freshly baked bread. It was more than he could resist. He immediately rented the room. The fact that it was on the third floor and not the most easily accessible room in the city of Chicago did not dismay him. Helen moved in to her sister Berniece's room.

Before long the widowed landlady and her large family took this bright young man into their hearts. They watched with amused delight as the romance blossomed. One Sunday evening, September 27, 1914, a glowing Helen announced that Doctor had proposed, she had accepted and they were engaged to be married.

During the soft, cool evenings of Indian summer, Helen often met Jacob at his office to walk home with him. Usually, eager to leave, he was relaxed and talkative, seeking release from the intense concentration of his long day's work.

One evening as the door closed behind his last patient, Jacob made no move to leave. Instead, he kissed Helen and said softly, "Sit down, I have something to show you."

He picked up a long envelope from his desk and waited with suppressed excitement as she read the enclosed letter.

Her eyes widened. "Doctor!" she gasped. "The college is asking you to teach two classes. It's the supreme compliment!"

"Think of it, Helen," his voice was thick with wonder. "Me—teaching medicine—in my own school."

"Why not?" She leaned over and grasped his hand. "They know you. They know you will be their finest teacher."

Jacob put his hand over hers. His words came slowly. "Life is changing for me, Helen. I will be successful. I know it. I even have a dream of, someday, starting my own sanitarium."

"Doctor, that's a beautiful idea."

"I'll need you to help me, Helen."

"Of course I'll help you."

"We'll never be rich, but I'll earn a good living. You will never want for anything. This I promise you. Helen, will you set the date for our wedding?"

A sudden wave of fear raced through her, and he felt the imperceptible stiffening of her fingers.

"Helen?" He tightened his hold on her hand.

She could not bring herself to reply. He placed his fingertips gently upon her face to read the emotions written there.

"You don't love me?"

She longed to cry out but could only press his fingers to her lips.

"Is it because I'm blind?"

"No," she whispered numbly. "No, no."

Suddenly he understood. "Children?"

She could hold back no longer. The tears and the words flowed as one. "Your parents had three blind children."

"And you're afraid our children will be blind?"

"Yes," her words were barely audible. "I'm afraid...I'm so afraid."

He sensed the depth of her agony. "You're right." He spoke lightly to mask his own enormous disappointment. "We should not have children."

She burst into uncontrollable sobs. Slowly, Jacob rose and drew her to him. With infinite tenderness, he brushed away her tears. "So be it, Helen. We will have no children."

After what Jacob impishly described as a whirlwind courtship, the date was set for Thanksgiving Day, November 25, 1914. Jacob was twenty-six years old.

CHAPTER 26

Louis and Faga, both devoutly orthodox, were overjoyed when Jacob told them of the impending marriage. Two children had married outside the Jewish faith, and the fact that Doctor would wed a Jewish girl gave them immeasurable happiness.

Faga was full of plans. "I knit for them two nice blankets and make a big, beautiful warm quilt. I already have everything I need. Still months till wedding, but tomorrow I begin."

The quilt was begun but never finished.

On October 14, when Helen came as usual to accompany Jacob home, the phone rang. Louis was calling from St. Luke's Hospital. Faga was being taken into surgery and she was asking for Jacob.

"We'll be there as fast as we can." Jacob's shock echoed the panic in his father's voice. The streetcar seemed to be taking forever. "We'll do better," he grumbled to Helen, "if we get out and push."

When they arrived Faga was dead. "Surgical shock," Dr. Weinstein called it. She had complained of such frightening, sharp pain in her side that he had immediately taken her to the hospital. An X-ray had revealed a suspicious lump on an ovary, and Weinstein believed it imperative to remove the lump at once. It was fairly routine surgery, but she had suddenly begun bleeding internally. Though they fought hard, they were unable to stop the loss of blood. The lump had proven to be malignant and the cancer was wide spread.

Dr. Weinstein's hands shook and his face was ashen as he reported this to Jacob. They were friends as well as colleagues. Weinstein had often conferred with Jacob about other patients. He was a good man. Jacob trusted him, but berated himself for giving in to his mother's modesty. Time after time, he had pleaded with Faga to allow him to examine her. With an embarrassed little smile, she always replied, "No, Doctor, it's not nice for son to examine mama. I'll go to Dr. Weinstein."

She was buried in the Forest Park Cemetery. Professor Bamberger delivered the eulogy. She was forty-seven years old.

Louis never ceased mourning for his beloved Fagale.

As Thanksgiving Day approached, Louis tried to focus upon the impending marriage.

"My son," he said, embracing Jacob, "you give your papa great joy. Don't worry about wedding. Everything I arrange — the rabbi — the minyan..." [A minion is a quorum of ten men who serve as witnesses in Orthodox Jewish tradition.]

"No, Papa! No minyan!"

"No minyan?" Louis was thunderstruck. "What you saying?"

"I'm saying, I'll make my own arrangements with the rabbi. We want a quiet, private wedding."

"But who will be witnesses? How you have Orthodox wedding without ten witnesses?"

"Papa, we don't want an Orthodox wedding. And under no circumstances will we have a minyan."

"So, my son, you have decided. May you have long happy life." But even as he spoke, Louis began making plans of his own.

On November 27, Helen and Jacob arrived at the rabbi's home for the performance of simple marriage rites. All was serenely quiet. The ceremony began. Without warning, from closets and bedrooms, out popped ten Jewish men. The triumphant father had arranged his minyan.

One year later, almost to the day, on November 29, 1915, Jacob was examining patients at a Municipal Sanitarium when a call came from Helen. Louis had been rushed to Washington Hospital with a diagnosis of bronchial pneumonia.

During the long, seemingly interminable journey to the hospital, Jacob was plunged into abysmal guilt. He knew Louis had developed a chronic cough and shortness of breath.

"Papa," he had pleaded, "let me examine you. You may have a touch of bronchitis."

"I fine!" Louis laughed. "Sick patients you examine. Me? I live to be a hundred."

Moving into a new flat with Helen, busy with patients, he had given in much too easily to his father's refusal for medical attention. And now Louis had bronchial pneumonia. It was fatal; there was no cure for pneumonia. Jacob could only hope he would get to the hospital in time to say goodbye.

Louis had survived only an hour after entering the hospital. Gasping for breath as he lay dying, he had asked Helen to tell Jacob how proud he was of him, and how much he loved him.

Louis, fifty-nine years old, was buried beside his beloved Faga.

CHAPTER 27

As Jacob's reputation for excellence spread throughout the city, his practice grew rapidly. The time had come to leave Van Teslaar, who was inordinately proud of his good friend's popularity. Jacob opened his own office in the Field Annex Building at 732 N. State Street., in downtown Chicago. Each day found it packed with patients. He was in constant demand for consultations by other physicians and hospitals were vying for his services.

People marveled at Jacob's accuracy at diagnosis. He astounded physicians and patients alike with his uncanny ability to take temperatures and pulses.

"How can you examine a patient you cannot see?" the curious never stopped asking.

Jacob always answered patiently, "My fingers are good eyes. With them, I search a patient's chest for depressions or enlarged glands. With them, I can detect diseases of the lungs. It is easy because, you see, the skin above an infected lung has quite a different feel from that of healthier portions of the body.

"Also, by placing both hands on the chest while the patient fills his lungs with air, my fingers note any disturbances the inhalation causes. Of course, like other physicians, I tap the chest with my fingertips and explore with the stethoscope. Then I listen with my ears, for they are sensitive to every little sound within the body. They tell me clearly when the machinery of the heart or digestive organ is not running smoothly. If there is a catch or obstruction in the lungs, my ears tell me immediately what is the cause and then I know what to do."

The phenomenal memory Jacob developed served him well. By merely placing his hands on any of his 3,500 patients or simply hearing the patient's voice, he could instantly recall the name and exact medical history of the case.

All of his medications, records, and accounts were done with Braille type he fashioned himself. There was never a chance of giving a wrong medication because all his bottles and boxes were marked with Braille as well as regular labels. An expert typist, he wrote his prescriptions on the small five-pound Bennett typewriter he carried with him so that the Latin symbols and abbreviations were clear and precise.

The subsequent history of the thousands of patients he examined and treated through the years are recorded in the files of the hospitals and clinics in which he worked. In every case, Jacob's diagnosis was proven correct.

On November 26, 1921, a request for information regarding the accuracy of the blind physician was sent to the ORNDOFF CHEMICAL LABORATORY at the Frances Willard Hospital. B. N. Orndoff, director of the laboratory and consulting Roentgenologist at the Municipal Tuberculosis Sanitarium, sent this response:

> "I have had abundant opportunity to check the results of Dr. Bolotin's examinations in our laboratory, which have included X-ray, pathological, and bacteriological examinations, and I do not hesitate to say that we have learned to respect the accuracy of his conclusions and diagnoses on conditions of the thorax as being of the very first order, and I have also had the opportunity to see his work and to know of his work in different institutions, and am pleased to state that I know he can deliver the goods.
>
> "The phenomenal accuracy with which this blind man is able to conduct his work, seems to depend upon two thing: first, the unusual development of the faculties of memory, touch, hearing, etc.; second, the remarkable assistance and record-keeping of his wife."

Jacob's ears not only diagnosed human ailments but his automobile's as well. He was able to confound garage mechanics by correctly detailing the malfunction of his Oldsmobile.

Teaching was important to Jacob, and he thoroughly enjoyed lecturing three mornings a week at his alma mater, the

Chicago College of Medicine and Surgery. His classes were exceptionally successful and other schools invited him to join their faculties. He accepted the positions of Lecturer on Diagnosis and Diseases of the Chest at Jenner Medical College; Chair of Diagnosis at the Chicago School of Medicine, and Professor of Physiology at the Progressive Preparatory School. He agreed to conduct a special lecture series for doctors on diseases of the heart and lungs, as well as tri-weekly classes for nurses at Frances Willard Hospital. He even conducted classes for a group of dentists to teach them how to handle a heart attack.

Three days a week, he worked at the Chicago Municipal clinics and sanitariums, and spent his evenings traveling about the city making house calls.

Still, he was not satisfied and drove himself incessantly. When, in January 1916, an opening for the position of Tuberculosis Physician for the city schools was offered by the Civil Service Commission, Jacob decided to take the examination. Unable to have children of his own, he longed for the privilege of working with children.

Again, newspaper editors sent reporters to cover the unusual story. One wrote:

BLIND PHYSICIAN WINS HIGH GRADE IN MERIT TEST

Two hundred ninety-six persons took the examination. Dr. Bolotin dictated his answers, and in spite of this handicap, he passed tenth with an average of 85.4 and is one of thirty school tuberculosis physicians appointed by the commission. His duties will be to examine school children for first signs of the insidious disease.

Helen begged Jacob not to accept the teaching position. "Why are you driving yourself this way?" she pleaded. "You cannot take on all the tuberculosis patients in the city of Chicago by yourself."

"Helen, the schools need doctors."

"Your patients need you! There are not enough hours in the day for all you must do now. What will your patients do if your health breaks down?"

Finally persuaded by Helen's arguments, Jacob refused the civil service offer. But he enjoyed the challenge of civil service examinations and continued to take them from time to time "to keep in practice," always refusing the positions won.

CHAPTER 28

Jacob was now nationally prominent. He had finally paid off his debt to Fred for his years of support and his financial future glowed brightly, but it was not to last.

Europe was in a state of upheaval. England and Germany were at war. Though President Wilson issued a proclamation of the neutrality of the United States on August 14, 1914, the American people, bombarded by propaganda from both sides, were bitterly divided.

Jacob was deeply troubled by the thought of his beloved country at war. He told Helen that if it really happened, he'd find some way to be of use.

On May 7, 1915, a German submarine horrified the world by sinking the great ocean liner, the *Lusitania*, in the Atlantic with the loss of 1,153 lives, among them 128 Americans. By 1916, it was clear that America would probably be drawn into the European Conflict.

President Wilson tried valiantly to avoid the turmoil and won reelection with the slogan, "He kept us out of war," but the rapid escalation of events inevitably forced Congress to act. On April 6, 1917, the United States declared war against Germany. Draft boards were established and thousands of young men enlisted.

"I'm going to enlist," Jacob announced to Helen. Both he and Fred presented themselves to the draft board where they were immediately rejected.

"What did you expect?" Helen laughed. "The Army does-n't need blind soldiers."

"No," Jacob replied quietly, "but I'm sure they can use blind doctors."

Early the next morning, he was at the draft board closest to his home. An orderly led him to the office of the Colonel in charge who was speaking on the telephone.

"Yes, I understand. Of course, I understand."

Jacob caught the frustration and weariness in his voice.

"A financial burden. Yes, well," the Colonel sighed, "perhaps another time. Thanks anyway. Goodbye."

As he hung up the phone, the orderly saluted. "Sir, this gentleman wishes to speak with you." He did a smart about-face and left the office.

The Colonel looked up, saw the cane and gasped, "Dr. Bolotin! It is Dr. Bolotin, isn't it?"

"Yes," Jacob smiled. "I'm Dr. Bolotin."

"I attended your lecture at Jenner College," the Colonel exclaimed as he stood up, "about a year ago. This is, indeed, an honor. What can I do for you?"

Jacob shook his head. "No, sir. It's what I can do for you? I'm here to offer my services, to be useful in any way I can."

The Colonel began to chuckle, picked up a pad of paper and pressed it into Jacob's hand.

"It's really amazing. On that pad are the names of doctors I've been calling. Your name is on tomorrow's list... and here you are."

"Why were you going to call me?"

"We are in urgent need of doctors to examine recruits for TB. We know that's your specialty. We also know how very busy you are. Would you, could you find time to serve on the Army Tuberculosis Board of Examiners?"

"Find time?" Jacob was jubilant. "I'll make time! Just tell me where and when."

It was a position Jacob held for the duration of the war. Though he spent exhausting days examining long lines of men and was forced to give up many of his own patients, he was supremely happy. His passionate love for America was satisfied. He was doing "his bit" for his country.

Coming home tired and happy after a long difficult day, Helen served him dinner. Then, making no attempt to hide her elation, she thrust a letter into his hand.

"It's from the United States Council of National Defense in Washington, D.C. They want your autobiography."

"They want my autobiography? Why?"

"They want to include it in an inspirational booklet they are distributing to the armed forces. Think of it, Doctor! The story of your life will be read by millions of American soldiers."

Jacob shoved the letter aside. "Yes, it's very flattering, and I'm glad it makes you happy, Helen. But to me what's really important in my life is that a blind man can be useful to our government."

He reached for her hand and pressed it to his cheek. "That," he said slowly, "and you have made it all worthwhile.

Jacob sent a brief autobiography to Washington. On December 12, he received a letter stating:

COUNCIL OF NATIONAL DEFENSE
WASHINGTON

December 12, 1917
Thank you for your letter of December 5th contain-
ing your autobiographical sketch. It is indeed an inspi-
ration, and will find its place in the little "Cheer-up fel-
lows" book which we are preparing.

> *Sincerely yours,*
> *James Bordley, Major, M.O.RC.*
> *Chairman, Sub-Committee on*
> *Ophthalmology*
> *Council of National Defense*

Stories and pictures of Jacob were now appearing in periodicals as far away as China.

One day, the postman delivered an unusual stack of booklets to the Chicago College of Medicine. Dr. Clutton, who was enormously proud of the growing adulation heaped upon Jacob, shouted with glee.

"Look at this!" He plopped a booklet on Miss Manning's desk. "I can't wait to show these to Dr. Bolotin."

"Well," his secretary laughed, "you'd better hurry. I just saw him pass our office on his way to the door."

"Oh!" Clutton grabbed some booklets and dashed down the corridor. "Dr. Bolotin!" he called. "Just a minute! Please! Just a minute, I have something for you."

Jacob stopped at the door and turned to face the excited registrar.

"Here," Clutton pressed a booklet into Jacob's hands. "These just came today.

"They're testimonials from the Corona Typewriter Company. And Doctor, you're in there right along with Jack London and a bunch of famous people. I think Mrs. Bolotin will be pleased."

Helen was pleased, but not surprised. She simply added them to the boxes already overflowing with newspaper clippings, magazine articles, letters and cards from all over the world that were stacked in a closet.

She was surprised and delighted when a beautifully wrapped package arrived from the New York Publishing firm of Grosset and Dunlap.

"It's a new novel," she told Jacob, "called *Silver Sandals.*"

Jacob was puzzled. "Why would they be sending us a novel?"

Quickly scanning the preface, Helen began giggling. "For a very good reason. It's about a blind detective. To make him believable, he wrote a long preface about you and Helen Keller. Would you like to hear any of it?"

"Sure," Jacob grinned, "why not?"

"Okay. I'll skip a lot of introduction about misconceptions of blindness, which you don't need. Then he goes on:"

"Have you heard or seen the wonderful Helen Keller?"

"Helpless, a thousand times no! Helpful is the word...Her all enduring optimism has made her one of the best-loved women in the world."

"Then he writes about you."

"Have you heard of America's wonderful blind diagnostician, Dr. Jacob Bolotin, of Chicago? Born blind, he has acquired physical abilities that seem absolutely superhuman."

"There's a two-page list of all the things you do. Then he asks:"

"Would you believe these things if you read them in a fiction story? Yet, every fact can be verified by the physician himself or any of his hundreds of friends."

"That guy," Jacob laughed, "knows more about me than I do."

Helen nodded her head. "He's very clever. He knew no one would believe a blind detective, so he simply borrowed the very real accomplishments of two real people—Helen Keller and you."

CHAPTER 29

The war was still raging in Europe when, seemingly out of nowhere, in May 1918, the world was plunged into a mysterious pandemic called the Spanish Influenza. Nothing of such magnitude had occurred in human memory. From the southern tip of Africa to the frozen Canadian arctic, no country escaped the avalanche of dead and dying.

In the United States, by mid-October the disease reached its most virulent peak and tens of thousands were dying weekly. During the last week in October, 2,700 Americans died "Over There" in battle against the Kaiser's army. That same week, 21,000 Americans died of influenza in the United States. Hospitals were stretched beyond capacity. Pine coffins were stacked high in cemeteries that had run out of space for graves or men to dig them.

Chicago was hit hard. In that city alone, on October 17, to be known forever as "Black Thursday," 400 people died.

Jacob found himself whirling in the depths of the cauldron. His days and nights became a blur of rushing from patient to patient, going without food or sleep, while trying to keep up his duties at the draft board, clinics and sanitariums, as well as responding to frantic pleas for help from other physicians.

"Jake," Dr. Weinstein phoned to ask, "you remember Millie Rosen? Her heart is going crazy, and so am I. Can you possibly spare a few minutes to check her out? 9710 West Flourney, third floor."

"Dr. Bolotin," the voice on the next call was hesitant. "I need your help."

"Of course, Dr. Beck," Jacob instantly recognized the voice of a doctor attending his lectures on Diseases of the Lungs. "What's the problem?"

"That's just it. I don't know. I'm hearing strange sounds in her lungs."

"Pneumonia?"

"Please come, Bolotin. I need your ear. North Chicago Hospital, Room 310."

"I'll be there fast as I can."

"No!" Helen was infuriated. "Tell them no! You're overloaded with your own patients. You don't need to take on theirs. For three days you haven't had a chance to change your clothes. You can't go on like this."

He would never admit it, but Jacob knew better than anyone else the crushing strain the epidemic was having on his health. He knew he was functioning on willpower alone. Yet it was impossible for him to slow down or deny a call for help.

Hurrying home at two in the morning to change his suit a tiny boy had covered with vile-smelling green vomit before he died, Jacob's fury and frustration erupted.

"This is war!" he raged. "We doctors are fighting a war just as much as our men overseas. But they've got weapons— they've got guns and bullets and cannons and bombs. We've got nothing. Medicines don't work. There's no vaccine. Our bombs are alcohol baths! Our bullets are aspirins! We're helpless! We're fighting with bare hands and liquids! That child died. I couldn't save him. They're dying so fast I can't save them! I can't save them!"

Helen listened in amazement. Never before had she seen Jacob so distraught.

"You're a doctor—not a god," she said quietly, trying to soothe him. "You can't save the whole world."

As Jacob put on his shoes, the phone rang and he heard Helen's cry of surprise.

"It's Moe, Doctor. It's Moe!"

"Moe?" Moe was Jacob's good friend and favorite pinochle buddy. "Are you calling from Seattle?"

"No," Moe replied. "We just got back home."

"What happened? I thought you and Ruthie went to celebrate your anniversary there."

"Doctor, you won't believe this. We saw it before we got to Seattle. Wagons loaded with coffins at every crossing, stacks of coffins at every depot. In Seattle, cops and people were wearing white masks. When we got off the train, bodies were stacked like sausages all along the station walls. The stench made Ruthie vomit. Damn good thing we had round-trip tickets. We took the next train back."

"Are you and Ruthie okay?"

"That's why I'm calling. Everyone on the train was coughing and sneezing; Ruthie must have caught the flu. Her chest and head are hurting something awful—her face is burning hot."

"Moe, if you have some alcohol, sponge her body with it now. Right now! If not, go get some. I'll be there as fast as I can."

He was on the stairway when Helen called him back to the phone. Bamberger's voice was tense and urgent.

"Jake, I know it's late, but it's Leah, my little granddaughter. She's having great difficulty breathing. The thermometer says 104.5. You're the only doctor I can trust."

"Pour some liquids down her, bathe her with alcohol, but don't let her get chilled. I'll be there as fast as I can."

Helen blocked his way, arms outstretched. "That's two of them! That means hours. First, you eat!"

"Helen, you know every minute counts. I'll eat later."

"You're not budging out of here till you get some food down you."

Jacob was too tired to argue. Besides, he had to admit he was hungry. The hot food tasted good and he ate rapidly. As he kissed Helen goodbye, she handed him a towel-wrapped bundle. "Here. It's hot chicken soup for Ruthie."

Moe was waiting for him in the vestibule. The alcohol bath had brought Ruthie's fever down. She was feeling better.

"Hello, Ruthie." Jacob felt her forehead, it was rough and hot. He groped for her hand, "Can I still say Happy Anniversary?"

She opened her eyes. "Hello, Doctor," she whispered. "I told Moe not to bother you.

"Well," Jacob laughed. "You know Moe. He's a stubborn mule that never listens. That's why he always loses at pinochle. But, I'm glad he did."

A quick examination revealed a steady pulse and a temperature of 100°. He placed his ear on her chest. Still slight congestion, but no pneumonia. Jacob was relieved. She would recover.

"Head hurt?" he asked.

"Yes, and my arms hurt."

"These aspirins will help and some of Helen's good, hot chicken soup. Helen's soup always cures everything. You'll be fine."

He turned to Moe. "Alcohol bath and two aspirins every three hours, and keep pouring liquids down her. Stop worrying, she's on the way up. I'm going to Bamberger's. Call if you need me."

As he dragged himself up the stairs to Bamberger's third floor apartment, the Professor's words kept ringing in his head. "You're the only doctor I can trust."

Trust? Jacob didn't trust himself. Though he gave dozens of alcohol baths every day, prescribed mountains of aspirins and oceans of liquids, patients were still dying. He raged incessantly at his inability to save them all. Each death was his personal failure, each recovery a miracle. Maybe, little Leah would be such a miracle.

The child was deep in coma when Bamberger led him to her bed. Too late for aspirins or liquids, her breathing was fast and labored. All Jacob could do was sponge the little pale face with alcohol and moisten her dry lips, a process he repeated constantly as the hours passed while, together, he and Bamberger sat and waited.

The Professor prayed softly in Hebrew, and Jacob wished he could understand the words. For the first time he became aware of a terrible inner loss, At Jacksonville he had been as removed from the world as in a convent. Aside from the biblical stories, he knew nothing of Judaism and had never even had a Bar Mitzvah. He envied the strength and calm that emanated from Bamberger, while he sat consumed with worry.

Dawn began streaking through the windows when Leah suddenly sat up, opened her eyes, grabbed the end of her long blonde braid, and cried out, "It's pointed! It's pointed!" Jacob knew the child would live.

As he described little Leah's remarkable recovery to Helen an hour later, she was startled to see tears of joy running down his cheeks. She knew the intense emotional reaction was caused by complete physical exhaustion.

"Doctor," she said gently, "go to bed and get some sleep. I'll call the draft board and tell them you won't be there today."

"Never!" Jacob was horrified. "That's my job. Of course I'll be there. I'll just lay down for a nap before I go."

Too tired to undress, he loosened his collar, fell down on the bed and was asleep before Helen could remove his shoes.

He was the only doctor at the draft board that morning. Three recruits came. One, wheezing and coughing, he immediately sent home with alcohol and aspirins.

When Jacob finally arrived at room 310 at the North Chicago Hospital that Dr. Beck had called him about the night before, the doctor was arranging for disposal of the body.

"She died ten minutes ago," he muttered. "You were right. Pneumonia. Not one member of her family is here; they're all sick." He wrapped his arms around Jacob. "Thanks for coming. I shouldn't have called you; there wasn't a darned thing you could do. I panicked. I've lost so many this month—I guess we never get used to it."

On the way to the elevator, Jacob heard his name called. It was Dr. Weinstein, the physician who took care of his parents. "Jake," he said, "Millie Rosen died. You were right when your ears caught the rales [an abnormal rattling sound in the chest] even my stethoscope didn't until they were so loud you could hear them across the street."

He said no more in the crowded elevator, and was silent until the hospital's massive front doors closed behind him. Then he clutched Jacob's arm and slumped heavily against the wall.

"I did everything I could. She was the fifth one this week, Jake. The fifth one!" He broke into deep, rasping sobs. "I wanted to be a doctor to cure people, not to watch them die."

"We're doctors, Sam, not gods. We try but we can't save everybody." Jacob found himself echoing Helen, putting aside his own anger and frustration to comfort his colleague.

"Her family is blaming me, Jake. They're actually blaming me. But I did all I could. I tried hard. Why, in God's name, isn't there a vaccine?"

"The labs are working on it. They're trying."

"Good! I'll tell my patients. Wait! Don't die! There may be a vaccine someday!"

Jacob was heartsick. He understood Sam's agony. Even if a vaccine was discovered, it would be too little and too late.

"We've just got to keep doing the best we can, Sam. This hellish epidemic can't last forever. It has to end. King Solomon said it three thousand years ago. 'This, too, shall pass.' Remember that, Sam. This, too, shall pass."

And pass it did. By the end of 1918, it vanished as mysteriously as it began, never to surface again. But in its brief seven months the Spanish Influenza, with its accompanying pneumonia, had succeeded in killing between twenty and forty million people worldwide, many more people than were killed during four long years of war.

No effective vaccine was ever discovered.

Miraculously, neither Helen nor Jacob fell victim to the disease.

CHAPTER 30

In early 1919 with the Influenza and war over, Jacob and Helen decided to make a change in their lives. One of Helen's sisters had been widowed ten years earlier. They knew she worked for subsistence wages and lived with her bright eleven-year-old son in one small room as she struggled to support them. Jacob and Helen had moved into a spacious flat as his practice continued to grow.

As they joined Helen's family at the Sabbath dinner table of her mother, Jacob turned to the boy, Alfred Perlman, and said, "Al, how would you like to come live with Aunt Helen and me?"

He grinned as he heard the boy's incredulous gasp. "I have already talked to your mother, and she is willing. Now, what about you?"

A few days later, Al and his mother moved into the Bolotins' sunny flat in a new, yellow brick building. The rooms were beautifully and tastefully decorated with the furniture carefully arranged to allow Jacob complete freedom of movement.

As soon as the boy moved in, Helen warned him that he was never to leave any of his belongings lying about for Jacob's safety.

"Al, you must remember," she said firmly, "Doctor knows where everything is. If you move anything, no matter what it is, you must always put it back exactly where it belongs."

The boy tried very hard, but one day shortly after his arrival Jacob slammed into a chair Al had left out of place. Both Jacob and the chair went crashing to the floor.

"Oh, my God!" Helen screamed as she flew to his aid.

Al stood rooted to the spot when he heard Jacob's cry of

pain. Slowly, Jacob untangled himself from the chair and rose from the floor. Helen helped him sit in a chair and quickly rolled up his trousers revealing how years of banging into obstacles had damaged them. Sores, ugly black and blue patches, huge scars and long red gashes covered every inch of skin. Gently, Helen applied antiseptics and bandages.

"How could you?" Helen's fury lashed at Al from her voice and eyes. "I told you! I warned you!"

"No, Helen, don't scold the boy!" Jacob shook his head reprovingly. "It was an accident. He didn't mean it." He reached out his hand to the boy. "It's all right." He drew Al to him and ran his fingers lightly over his face.

"So," he smiled, "you have had a good scare. Well, it wasn't the first fall I've had in my life. Don't worry, I'll be fine."

Soon Al became Jacob's constant companion.

Jacob loved birds, and for the first time in his life he could afford to have some of his own. He had a parrot named Pretty Boy and a canary named Dickie, who competed for attention with Pretty Boy. The parrot kept the whole family amused. Every morning, when Jacob opened his cage, Pretty Boy would scramble joyfully up his arm, perch on his shoulder and nibble his ear contentedly. Jacob loved the feel of the soft, feathered body against his cheek. Pretty Boy seemed to sense Jacob's blindness because he was much gentler with Jacob than with any other member of the household.

Sometimes a call would come in on a Saturday morning that preempted all plans for the next several hours.

"Doctor," the voice said, "this is Winkelman at The Fair. Got in a new shipment this week and they're singing their heads off."

Within an hour, Jacob and Al were at The Fair, one of Chicago's largest downtown department stores. Winkelman, in charge of the pet section, led Jacob into the center of the long aisles of birdcages. Here, entirely surrounded by the sweet chirping of two hundred canaries, Jacob would stand transfixed. It was as though he stood alone in some wild forest and the birds were singing just for him.

Al clearly adored Jacob, who in turn was thrilled to have a son that he had always wanted but could not allow himself and Helen to have. Though everyone in the family called him "Doctor," Al took to calling him "Doc." It was the closest Al dared to come to "Dad."

With Al's arrival in the household, a new routine was established. Al got home from school around three-fifteen and immediately finished his homework. At about five o'clock every afternoon, Jacob and Helen arrived home from his office and house calls. After cleaning up, Jacob went into the sun parlor and seated himself in his large, brown leather chair that stood beside the window. As the late afternoon sunshine flooded over him, he would lift his face to the sun with a deep sigh of contentment and murmur, "The sun is beautiful." As he settled back in his chair, Al read the headline of each story in the Chicago Daily News aloud to him. Jacob would say "Read," if there were any he wanted to hear. They usually finished most of the news section before Helen called them to dinner. After eating, they returned to the sun parlor where Al would read aloud from the classics until his bedtime, nine o'clock.

Jacob passed on an intense love of literature to his young nephew. He patiently would stop Al to correct his pronunciation or explain the meaning of a word. And he found it satisfying to be able to revisit many of his favorite books in a way that was broadening the horizons of his nephew at the same time.

Jacob often came home from his classes with his briefcase bulging with examination papers, which Al also read to him. The medical terms were difficult tongue twisters for the boy, but if he came out with a reasonable facsimile of the sound, Jacob would say it aloud and they would go on. Al also read to him from the American Medical Association Journal, a task that he shared with Helen.

Helen now served as Jacob's assistant, reading the blood pressure dials during examinations, keeping meticulous records and case histories, chauffeuring him in their Oldsmobile and accompanying him everywhere. Jacob was extremely proud of Helen, who had learned to read Braille, and often referred to her as his eyes.

The only area of conflict they had stemmed from Helen's mania for perfection. Helen could not bring herself to leave the flat if anything was half done or undone. All had to be in perfect order. Jacob, at times, was not the most patient of men. When he was ready to leave, he wanted to go quickly. Though he always gave Helen ample warning of the departure time, she could seldom get ready as promptly as he wanted. Jacob would walk downstairs to the rear garage to wait for Helen. Inevitably, before she came down, Jacob had his finger on the bell, ringing it like a fire alarm, while he yelled, "Hurry, Helen, hurry!" This would throw her into near hysteria and only add to the delay. Then the neighbors would hear the bellowing "H-E-L-E-N!" go careening up the stairwell loudly enough to shatter glass. Sometimes, after several more moments of waiting with Al, Jacob would say, "Al, let's go!" and away they would go by streetcar.

These incidents created many unhappy moments. Helen did not trust Jacob's ability to travel alone in spite of all the years during which he had managed perfectly. Nor did she trust anyone other than herself to accompany him.

Among Jacob's greatest pleasures were riding in the car and good food. As often as his schedule permitted, Helen, Jacob and Al spent Sundays taking leisurely drives into the countryside. Jacob loved the sweet smells of freshly mown hay and meadows fragrant with clover and wild flowers. With his extraordinary sense of smell, he enjoyed announcing that they were approaching a stream, a farm or a forest, a prairie or a cornfield, and of course, he was always right.

The outing, capped with dinner at one of the many fine roadhouses, refreshed Jacob and provided the respite he needed.

Many a Saturday afternoon would find the family at Gold's, a Mecca for Chicago gourmets. No matter how crowded the dining room, a waiter always materialized to lead them to a table. Seating them ceremoniously, he would whip out his pad and announce as he wrote:

"Three T-bone steaks, a big bowl of French fries, lemon cream pie for the young gentleman, apple pie for Dr. and Mrs. Bolotin." Then he would pause, pencil in midair, and ask with a grin, "Or is it strawberry shortcake this time, Doctor Jake?"

The waiters were devoted to Jacob who examined them without charge, as he did countless other patients. No person was ever turned away because of inability to pay. He simply never received a bill.

A block from the flat, on the corner of Harrison Street and Independence Boulevard, was Hookway's Pharmacy. Its ancient, polished, wooden counters and shelves, filled with old-fashioned jars and bottles, were decorated with a huge bronze mortar and pestle and the traditional apothecary jars, tall and slender, glowing with colored water. Near the door stood a glass case laden with long licorice whips, twisted peppermint sticks, jellybeans and other mouth-watering delights of child-hood.

Hookway, a tall, lean man with graying hair and mustache, idolized the Doctor. Whatever the Bolotins purchased was always "On Special" that day. "Cash and carry prices," Hookway informed them blandly.

Jacob was extremely fond of Hookway and found excuses to visit him almost daily. Often he would walk to the pharmacy to await Helen and seat himself on the long wooden bench that stood just inside the doorway. Hookway would instantly drop whatever he was doing, sit down beside Doc, and the two men would chat happily until Helen arrived.

When Hookway learned Jacob was troubled about missing phone calls while he was away, he clapped him on the shoulder and announced, "Doctor, your worries are over! I'll have an extension line put in from my phone to yours. That way, I can keep a record of all your calls."

"Absolutely not!" Jacob replied. "You're running a business, not a phone service. Besides, extension lines must be expensive. It's good of you to offer, but forget it."

"Oh!" Hookway's voice was brittle and angry. "I thought we were friends. I sure never expected you to deny me a chance to earn a bit of extra money." He rose and began walking away.

"Hey! Wait a minute!" Jacob exclaimed. "Who's doing who a favor here?"

"Favor?" Hookway snorted, "Of course not. You think I'd do it for nothing? I'm no fool. I'd charge you for every call. The more calls you get, the richer I get."

"And the more bookkeeping you'll have," Jacob retorted.

"Yep!" Hookway muttered dryly sarcastic. "I might be interrupted selling licorice sticks or a jar of pills."

"Hookway, you sly old goat! You have the damnedest way of twisting things. But," Jacob added thoughtfully, "it would be nice. Tell you what. Let me pay for the extension line and it's a deal."

The line was installed and was probably the first answering service in the history of Chicago.

CHAPTER 31

By the beginning of 1919, the city of Chicago breathed a sigh of relief. Normalcy was, once again, the order of the day.

Seven months later a race riot plunged the city into chaos. The sun rose early on Sunday, July 27, 1919, and was perhaps the catalyst that sparked the rioting. By 10 AM heat waves could be seen rising from the streets, and children were frying eggs on the sidewalks.

A black boy, seeking relief from the stifling heat, decided to take a swim in Lake Michigan's cooling waters. As he swam around he unknowingly crossed the invisible line segregating the beach. White youths, affronted by the intrusion, began yelling and motioning him away, but the boy in the lake could neither see nor hear them. Angered, the whites began pelting him with a hail of stones.

Immediately, blacks on the beach retaliated by hurling stones at the whites. The boy, unable to swim ashore, clung desperately to a small piece of floating railroad tie. Either he weakened and lost his grip on the log or a stone knocked him unconscious [the stories vary]. He sank beneath the water and drowned.

As the infuriated blacks pulled his body ashore, they commanded the beach policeman to arrest the whites responsible for his death. The officer refused. Prudently and quickly, he left the scene.

Attracted by the uproar, indignant crowds gathered and a full-scale fight erupted that spread as fast as the influenza had across Chicago. Distorted rumors inflamed the city:

"A black man had been lynched and hung from a downtown building."

"A white woman had been attacked and mutilated by a black."

"A Negro woman had been killed, her breasts ripped off, and her infant had been killed by having his brains dashed out against a wall."

Violence escalated with every incident. Angry mobs raced through the streets killing and maiming citizens solely on the basis of the color of their skin.

For thirteen days, Chicago was without law and order, despite the fact that by the fourth day, the state militia had been called in. The toll at the end left 38 dead [23 blacks, 15 whites], and 537 injured. Many black homes were burned and hundreds of people were made homeless.

The original thirteen days gave birth to sporadic episodes of bloody violence destined to rage for years in the large section of Chicago's South Side known as the "Black Belt."

After a time, the riots subsided only to flare up again months later. In the heart of this area, on 46th Street and south Wabash Avenue, stood the Municipal Tuberculosis Dispensary. Jacob, serving as attending physician at the dispensary, paid no attention to the reports of stabbings, beatings and holdups of whites entering the area. It never occurred to him to request a transfer to another section of the city or to stop coming to the dispensary. Tuberculosis was rampant among the blacks, and Jacob knew they needed him.

Suddenly, one week the tensions tightened. Whites driving through the area were stopped, dragged from their cars, beaten, and sometimes killed. During the height of the fighting, Jacob's day at the clinic arrived. Frightened, Helen pleaded with him not to go. Jacob was adamant. He was convinced the blacks would never harm him and would let him walk freely in and out of the area as long as they knew who he was. But he refused to allow Helen to drive him there in the car as she usually did because they would appear only as whites and go unrecognized. He decided that he and Al would go by streetcar.

They got off the streetcar two blocks from the dispensary. A small group of black men, lounging about the corner, straightened and began strolling toward them. Jacob and Al continued walking slowly forward. Al was terrified but tried not to show it as he walked with Jacob, his hand resting on his uncle's arm.

Then the men surrounded them and one stood in front blocking the way.

"Hello, Doctor Jake," he said. "You going to the dispensary?"

"Of course," Jake replied coolly.

"Aintcha fraid?"

"Why should I be afraid of my friends?"

"We didn't expect you."

"This is my day."

"Yes, sir," the man smiled and tipped his hat. "This is your day. This is sho your day."

The remainder of the two-block walk was a triumphal procession, as every black person Jacob and Al passed greeted them warmly, and many stopped to identify themselves.

Because of the love and respect of these black people, trapped in their hellish ghetto, Jacob and Al were able to walk safely through that dangerous, explosive area.

As they approached the dispensary they saw six National Guardsmen, armed with pistols and machine guns, stationed on the long white porch that covered the front of the one-story wooden building. The guardsmen stood in shocked silence, stunned disbelief on their faces, as they stared at the white boy leading a blind white man along the sidewalk as calmly as though they were strolling through a park. Shaking their heads in bewilderment, they stepped respectfully aside as Jacob and his nephew entered the building.

Tom, the black attendant who had worked for years at the dispensary, came to see who had opened the door. "Doctor Jake!" he gasped, "I never thought I'd see you today. How didja get here?"

"We walked," Jake replied serenely, enjoying his consternation.

"Walked! All the way from the streetcar...by yourselves?"

"Of course. How else would we get here?"

"Didntcha know you coulda been killed?" Tom reached for Jake's hat. "Yes, sir!" he nodded his head admiringly, "I shoulda known you'd make it some way. Yes sir, I shoulda known."

The news of Jacob's presence at the dispensary spread with the speed of a streaking comet, and patients came in a steady stream throughout the day. It was dark when he finished examining his last patient, a small boy ill with tuberculosis, brought in by his grandmother. The old woman took Jacob's hand and placed within it a bulky, carefully wrapped package.

"Bless you, Doctor Jake," she murmured softly. "Bless you."

As Jacob and Al left the clinic, four tall black men quietly joined them on the sidewalk. They made no attempt at conversation, just followed a short distance behind.

Jacob realized instantly that, worried for his safety in the dark, dimly lighted streets, they had appointed themselves his bodyguards. As people passed them on the walk back to the streetcar, it was a chorus of, "Evenin', Doctor Jake," "Howdy, Doctor Jake," "Thanks for comin', Doctor Jake." When the streetcar arrived, Jacob and Al felt themselves lifted up and hoisted onto the back platform. As they turned to thank the men, the men grinned broadly. "Evenin', Doctor Jake," they said, "See ya next time," and waved as the car pulled away.

When Helen opened the package, it contained a cucumber, an acorn squash and a jar of homemade plum jam.

CHAPTER 32

In sharp contrast to his clinic patients, Jacob had many wealthy patients who lived outside the city and paid his expenses to travel to their homes. Several lived across Lake Michigan in Benton Harbor and South Haven, Michigan. Rather than go by car or train, Jacob always chose to go by ship.

Many evenings Jacob, Helen and Al boarded a ship at the old Graham and Morton dock to make the overnight crossing. Jacob passionately loved the sea and ships. His senses were exhilarated by the sound of the waves, the feel of wind and spray on his skin, the rolling and pitching of the ship.

A thunderous gale struck suddenly during one crossing. Giant waves and wild winds tossed the huge vessel around like helpless driftwood. Passengers fled to their cabins, miserably seasick. Jacob remained on deck thoroughly enjoying the storm, laughing and shouting at every lurch and crash of the careening ship. Finally, long past midnight, he allowed Helen to coax him inside. He often spoke of that wondrous storm and hoped to experience another, but he never did.

People were amazed to learn that Jacob was an expert at pinochle. Those watching him play for the first time found it uncanny. They invariably asked how he did it.

Jacob was always happy to demonstrate the procedure and would send Al down to Hookway's to bring back a fresh pinochle deck. Then, as Al handed each card to Jacob and identified it, he would place it in his small Braille stylus and punch tiny, raised dots in opposite corners. During the game, he held his cards face down an inch or two above the table, with their backs to the other players, while his fingers moved imperceptibly over the Braille lettering. Each man called his moves aloud and Jacob, unerringly, remembered every play.

He often let Al sit beside him to manage his chips. One night he won an exceptionally large pot. While his friends lamented their losses, he turned to Al grinning gleefully.

"You see, Al," he said, "how easy it is to win with marked cards."

Jacob never forgot a name. After meeting a person for the first time, he was always able to recall his name, no matter how long a time had elapsed before meeting him again. The hand-clasp, the voice, the odor, even the height of the individual were his clues to identification.

His friends enjoyed making bets to see if they could fool him. One would slip into the room where Jacob was sitting and neither move nor speak. Within a few seconds, Jacob would call him by name. Or two friends would approach him and only one would speak. He loved these tricks and would go along with the ploy until the men were convinced they had succeeded. Then Jacob would casually turn and ask the silent one a question that would create gales of laughter. His seemingly psychic ability to sense the presence of people about him and identify them dumbfounded everyone. No matter how hard his friends tested him, no one ever caught him in an error.

It didn't matter where it was. In May of 1921, as he and Helen were getting off the train in Cincinnati, Ohio, a porter asked, "Can I help you with those bags, sir?"

"Thank you, Johnson," Jacob replied.

The amazed porter exclaimed, "You remember me?"

"Of course," Jacob said, "you were a patient at the Ashland Avenue Clinic."

"But that was nearly four years ago. How could you…"

"Your name is Clemons Johnson, and you were a very sick boy. I'm glad to find you working."

"You fixed me up good, Doctor Jake. No, Mam!" he exclaimed, as Helen handed him a tip. "Thank you, but not from you!" He pushed the tip back into Helen's hand. "Doctor Jake helped me. Now I can help him."

Returning to his office after a busy morning at the clinic, a woman was waiting for him, "Dr. Bolotin. I'm not here as a patient. I've come because I owe you an apology."

Jacob unlocked the door, "Please come in and sit down, Mrs. Fenton."

She gasped, "You remember me?"

"Of course." He waited until she was seated, "Now, what's all this about an apology?"

"I can't believe you remember me! It's been so long ago."

"You brought Cassie, your daughter. She was my first patient in my first office. That was six years ago. She must be quite the young lady by now."

There was a momentary pause before she replied, "She's gone, Doctor."

"Gone?"

"Two days after we saw you, her appendix burst."

A hot surge of anger raced through Jacob. "I told you she needed immediate attention."

"Yes, you did."

"I warned you. I told you she had appendicitis."

"But I didn't believe you. When I saw you place your ear on Cassie's stomach, I suspected you were a fraud. And when you admitted you were blind, I knew I was right. I was furious. I was rude and ugly. I even accused you of falsifying your license."

"It was a natural reaction." Jacob was polite but seething inside.

"It was wrong. I know now how wrong I was." She paused. What she had come to say was not easy. Jacob heard the struggle behind every word. "The day we saw you her pain subsided, and we took her to another doctor. He told us to wait a few days to see if surgery was really necessary. In the middle of the night, she began screaming. We rushed her to the hospital and they took her right into surgery, but...," her voice trailed off into wracking sobs.

"But," he finished slowly, "it was too late."

"I sacrificed my sweet child to my prejudice, my ignorance. It's something I live with every day of my life."

Jacob was silent. After a moment, she continued in a dull monotone. "God made you blind for a purpose. I know that now." She paused, took a deep breath before she continued, "Several months ago, you saved Ada's son and little grandson from the flu after their doctor said nothing more could be done. It was like a miracle. I realized your blindness has made you not just a good doctor but a great doctor." Another pause. Then, softly, her voice wrapped in guilt, "I'm so ashamed. Cassie can't forgive me for being such a fool, but you can. That's why I'm here. Dr. Bolotin, will you accept my apology?"

Jacob ached for her. "Of course," he murmured as he groped for her hand.

She grasped his tightly and pressed it to her heart. "God bless you, Doctor. God bless you."

At the door, she turned back. "You might like to know," she spoke slowly, her words a heartbeat away from tears, "the last thing Cassie asked for was her kewpie doll."

CHAPTER 33

The voice of Dr. Jacob Bolotin was among the first raised to focus world attention upon the needs and rights of the handicapped and the underprivileged.

Dr. Copeland's well-meaning phone call was the innocent catalyst that dramatically and permanently changed Jacob's life.

"Jake," Copeland said, "we want you to be one of the speakers at our annual medical society convention. It's coming up in two months. That should give you plenty of time."

There was a long silence, Jacob had never refused to comply with any request from his beloved professor. But this one was different.

"Jake?"

"Yes, sir," Jacob stuttered.

"Did you hear me?'

"Yes, sir."

"Do you understand me, Jake? We want you to be the main speaker at the opening banquet."

"Main speaker? ... Opening banquet? ... Me?" Jacob could scarcely breathe.

"Yes. It's an unanimous decision by the convention committee."

"Dr. Copeland, please — I don't understand. You can get top professionals — famous people in any field you choose. The very best..."

"That's true, Jake. These people are always available and some will speak at the convention later on. But this year, to open the convention, we want something different. Not just to be entertained — something meaningful for everyone there. We want you."

"Meaningful?" Jacob was thoroughly confused. "You want a talk at a banquet on diseases of the heart and lungs?"

Copeland's laughter rang in Jacob's ear. "Hardly, Jake! We'll have plenty of that later."

"Then, what? What could you possibly want me to talk about?"

"You."

"Me?" He couldn't be hearing right. He asked again, "Me?"

"Yes, Jake. We're proud of you. We want to show you off"

"Because I'm blind?"

"Precisely. But not just because you're blind. Because you're a blind doctor, and a damn good one, and because of how you became a doctor. It's an absolute miracle. When you enrolled, we all wondered what kind of an idiot was this guy to think a blind man could become a doctor? You're not aware of the way you turned this college upside down, or how you've revolutionized the antiquated thinking of every doctor in Cook County. My boy, you've taught us all there's a helluva lot more to medicine than two good eyes. Jake? Are you listening?"

"Yes, sir."

"All we want you to do is just tell the story of your life."

"Why?"

"Because it's unique — an incredible, unbelievable story. It fascinated and amazed all of us, and it will fascinate and amaze every doctor at the convention."

"But I can't just stand there and talk about myself. It's too presumptuous — the height of arrogance. It's bragging, pure and simple."

"For someone else it might be bragging, but for you it's not bragging, it's fact. We know. We went through every step of the way with you. And there you are, standing before them, living proof that all you're saying is true. The committee is counting on you, Jake. Please, don't disappoint them."

Jacob was certain he had never been more miserable in his life. "Dr. Copeland, I want to please you more than you'll ever know. But please understand. I'm not a speaker. I haven't given a speech since I was a kid in Jacksonville fifteen years ago."

"Wrong, Jake. You're giving a speech every time you talk to your classes. Except we call them lectures."

"That's different. A classroom is filled with students. It's not a convention banquet filled with doctors."

Jacob heard Copeland's deep sigh, "Oh Jake, Jake! Sometimes I think you're blind in more ways than one." He paused. When he continued, his words came slowly, reluctantly, "I think this is the time to tell you something you don't know. Something I've never told you before. Maybe it will help you now. Jake, when you first began teaching, I often sat in on your classes."

"You! Sat in on my classes? Why?"

"Because the faculty was concerned how our students would respond to a blind professor and how you could conduct classes without a text, or notes or even a blackboard. "

"Did I pass the test?"

"With an A+!" Copeland chuckled. "But I must admit, some of the professors were pretty envious. They'd be lost without notebooks and outlines. Matter of fact," another chuckle, "so would I. Anyway, I still came often after that because I was intrigued by the way you presented your subject—AND—by the solid grip you had on every student's attention."

"Those were classes. Students had to pay attention."

"True, Jake, but there's another reason. Sitting in on your classes, I discovered something you're unaware of. You're a born speaker. You have a fine voice. You speak clearly and distinctly, no mumbling, no hem-and-hawing. What's more important, you speak with an intensity and passion for your subject that immediately commands and holds attention. It'll work the same way at the convention as it does in your classes."

Little thrills of joy raced through Jacob as he caught the unabashed affection and fatherly pride in Copeland's voice. How could he deny this beloved man? Somehow he had to make him understand.

"Forgive me, Dr. Copeland. I don't want to be difficult. Maybe this intensity and passion you speak of is because I'm talking medicine, a subject I love. I'm not talking about myself."

"But that's exactly what we want you to talk about. Your struggle at the college inspired all of us to try harder. People want to be inspired, Jake. Your story will inspire everyone at that convention and knock those doctors off their complacent butts. It will provide the excitement we need."

In despair, Jacob blurted, "Please, sir, tell me. Would you want to stand up there before all those doctors and talk about yourself?"

There was a long silence on the telephone before the professor replied, "Let's be honest, Jake." His words were strung carefully like beads upon a wire. "There are a thousand Dr. William Copelands in this country. There's only one Dr. Jacob Bolotin."

The silence that followed seemed to throb with a life of its own as Jacob sat too deeply moved to speak. Finally, Copeland's whisper broke the silence.

"Besides, I promised the committee you'd do it."

Jacob sat, turned to stone. A promise made could never be broken. He had to make sure.

"You promised?" he mumbled.

"Yes, Jake. I promised. The committee was so eager—I promised. I'm sorry. I should've checked with you first. It just never occurred to me you'd object."

"You promised?"

"I promised."

It was all over. He would never ask anyone to break a promise, least of all Copeland. There was no way out.

It was another challenge to be met. Somehow he'd do what he had to do.

"Shall I go sit on the hot seat, Jake?"

In spite of his fear, Jacob smiled. "'No, sir, that won't be necessary.

"Then you'll do it?"

"I'll never live up to your expectations. But I'll try my best."

"That's all we ask. We know you, Jake. Stop worrying. You'll do fine."

"Thank you, Dr. Copeland."

"Oh! One more thing, Jake. Can we stop this 'Dr. Copeland' bit? We aren't teacher and student anymore. You're a doctor. We're colleagues." He tried to toss it off lightly, but his words were full of emotion. "We're more that colleagues, we're friends. All my friends call me Bill. I'd really be pleased if you'd call me Bill."

"I'll try, sir."

"And no more 'Sir'! Makes me feel like an old man. Please, Jake. Just plain yes and no. Okay?"

"Yes, sir."

They both burst out laughing and the phone clicked off.

Fred whooped with glee when he heard about the invitation. "Go for it, Doctor. Copeland is no fool. He wouldn't have promised the committee if he didn't believe you could do it. And he got a unanimous okay. They really want you, Doctor. Go for it!"

CHAPTER 34

Jacob gave the speech. Filled with misgivings, initially afflicted by stage fright, he did what he was asked to do. Surprised by constant interruptions of applause and laughter, the misgivings and fright quickly vanished. He relaxed. Simply and honestly, he related the story of his life.

"We, the doctors of this great country," he said in conclusion, "hold in our hands the health, well-being, often the lives, and ultimately, the happiness of every human being in our land. It's a responsibility we chose, a responsibility we worked years to achieve. It's a frightening, awesome responsibility. It's a responsibility we are proud of.

"It has a name. Of all the great titles in this world, King, Prince, Rajah, Tsar, Emperor or Caesar, none is more meaningful, more important, more trusted, more beloved or beneficial to humanity than the little six letter title I am proud to share with you ... d-o-c-t-o-r ... Doctor."

Suddenly he heard the great scraping of chairs. He panicked. Was everyone leaving? Within seconds, Copeland's arms were around his shoulders.

"Wave to them, Jake. It's a standing ovation! Wave to them."

Jacob obediently waved his cane in the air and smiled happily and the prolonged applause mingled with cheers.

"You did it, Jake! You did it!" Copeland glowed with pride. "I knew you would!"

The delegates crowded around Jacob, shaking his hand, patting his shoulder, asking him to give his talk in their own hometowns. At the speaker's table, they lined up in front of Helen to give her their cards.

"Dr. Bolotin will hear from me. Everyone at home has got to hear that speech."

The story of Dr. Jacob Bolotin swept through the medical world with cosmic speed. Within a week after the convention

Jacob was inundated with requests from all over the country for "that speech." Three came from Canada, two from London. Requests from Brussels, Paris and Stockholm assured him if he couldn't deliver "that speech" in their language, a translator would be present.

The thought of traveling to Europe excited Jacob, but Helen brought him back to reality, to the restraints of time and cost. Reluctantly, he agreed to confine himself to the Midwestern states.

"That speech" begged for a title, and Jacob named it "Over the Top in Darkness" as a tribute to the battle cry memorialized during World War I when the American soldiers in France had climbed out of their muddy, rat-infested trenches and gone "over the top" to victory.

He quickly learned Copeland was right. People want to be inspired, to be lifted out of the monotonous routine of daily living. Jacob's speech was what they needed. Soon "Over the Top" was in constant demand and became one of the most famous speeches of the day. Now he was speaking almost every night in the week and sometimes two or three times in a single day.

Reporters were always present and every appearance elicited a glowing review.

By One Who Was There

It was too bad that the whole people of this city could not have heard the lecture given by Dr. Jacob W. Bolotin of Chicago Tuesday night.

He has never seen the light of day, but seems to be the center of light himself from the manner in which he radiates it to his audience. His struggle for an education puts to shame those who cry out over minor misfortunes and handicaps.

His speech was full of humor and wit. The audience swung from attacks of merriment to the opposite emotion when

eyes filled with tears and their owners
wondered how achievements of such
magnitude were possible.

He has surpassed Helen Keller with
his amazing ability to do things in which
the sense of sight is absolutely necessary.
There is no doubt, Dr. Bolotin will always
rank among the great blind people in history.

                              Edgerton, Wisconsin

Helen seldom read the newspaper accounts of his talks to
Jacob. She was afraid they might make him self-conscious, but
she was inordinately proud of the praise he received.

The press labeled his speech *Highly Inspirational – A Speech
of Great Power.*

This judgment puzzled Doc. "I don't understand it," he
confided to Fred. "Why is my life such a source of inspiration?
All I did was plow my way through obstacles to achieve my
goal. I'm proud of that, but why is it creating such a furor? You
did it. You fought the antagonism of the business world to create a shop of your own. Millions of people do it everyday."

"Sure," Fred replied, "lots of people do it, but how many do
it without eyes? I don't need eyes to sell brooms and pails and
mops. You didn't need eyes to sell typewriters. But to become a
doctor without eyes – that's the miracle. That's why people
respond like they do to your speech.

"Copeland explained it to you—and it took plenty of guts
to say what he did—'there are thousands of Dr. William
Copelands in this country, but there's only one Dr. Jacob
Bolotin.' That's why your talk is different, why people find it so
helpful. Keep at it, Doctor! Keep at it!"

There was no way he couldn't "keep at it." Every day new
batches of requests filled his mailbox at home and at his office.
Letters arrived constantly from people thanking him for giving
them the courage to overcome problems that had threatened
their marriages or their careers or their lives. Total strangers

bared their souls to him and revealed how his speech had helped them solve what had seemed insurmountable problems.

Jacob was pleased that people found "Over the Top" so inspiring, but it was obvious to those that knew him he was not enjoying it.

"No matter how you describe it," he grumbled, "I'm still talking about myself, and I don't like it."

Helen knew that Jacob had a consuming passion to alert the world to the needs of the handicapped and it would be only a matter of time before he found a way to express it.

It came sooner than she expected.

"Tonight," Jacob announced as they were preparing to leave, "my speech will be different."

Helen was alarmed. "Why?" she demanded. "People like it the way it is. Why do you want to spoil it?"

"I'm not spoiling it. I'm improving it."

"How? How can you possibly improve it?"

"You'll see," Jacob teased. "I think you'll like it."

The astute reporter, who had covered Jacob's speeches before, immediately caught the subtle change in focus. The next day his review announced:

BLIND DOCTOR GIVES POWERFUL PLEA FOR HANDICAPPED

Using innumerable clever remarks and bright stories which constantly kept his audience in a happy frame of mind, Dr. Jacob Bolotin, blind Chicago physician, delivered a powerful plea for a different attitude toward handicapped people. By offering in himself as the personal example of what may be accomplished against most discouraging and seemingly overwhelming odds with a mind determined to succeed in the great battle of life. He told of his daily struggle against the almost crushing handicap of sightlessness, and how with cheerfulness and determination he has made more than an ordinary success of an almost hopeless life, demonstrating again the truth of that old adage "Where there's a will there's a way."

"I am blind," he said, "and I am a doctor. The fact that I am standing here before you is living proof of what we, the handicapped, can achieve. The sentiment held by the average person that we are helpless, useless objects of charity must be erased forever.

"Of course, a blind man cannot drive a car, run a locomotive or paint pictures, or do anything that requires vision in every detail of the work. But a blind man can be principal of a school, president of a bank, Mayor of Chicago or President of the United States. Why not? These men work mentally. They direct. All the real labor is done by subordinates.

"No," he said, "the major problem for us is not our affliction, but the wall of ignorance, injustices, indifference and misconceptions that separate us from you who can see. We must break down that wall, but we can't do it alone. We need your help. The Bible commands us to love our brothers and sisters as ourselves. We, the handicapped, are your brothers and sisters. You are the soldiers in our battle to break down that wall. You must help us awaken the world to the needs and rights of the handicapped. You must care.

"How fortunate we all are to be citizens of this great country. Let us make its

> bounty, its freedoms and rights we take
> so for granted, available to every human
> being regardless of physical infirmities,
> rich or poor—equal rights to an educa-
> tion; equal rights to work; equal rights to
> dream and achieve that dream; to achieve
> lives of self-reliance, pride and usefulness
> to our fellow man, and to live to the
> fullest the life God granted him."

At last, Jacob was pleased with his speech. His enthusiasm and passion for his subject communicated itself to his audience, and he was in even greater demand than before.

Medical schools, medical societies and hospitals wanted lectures on medical subjects; schools wanted his talk on "Citizenship and Americanism"; fraternal and civic groups asked for "Over the Top"; and what came as a complete surprise to Jacob were the demands for commencement addresses by schools and universities on all levels. He often shared the speaker's platform with leaders of commerce, government, industry and the literary world. At a Chicago convention attended by 2,300 men from the United States and Canada, he found himself seated next to the prime minister of Canada. In a single day, he spoke to the Winnebago County Medical Society, a fraternal organization, a high school assembly and the Rockford College graduating class in Rockford, Illinois.

The impact he made upon the faculty and student body at the college was described in a letter from the president of the college, William A. Maddox:

> "I am sure you cannot realize what currents your philosophy of life stirred in all of us. It is hard for any of us to understand that any of us can profoundly affect our fellows, but I assure you that you did."

People from all walks of life enjoyed giving Jacob gifts to express their appreciation. One created a funny situation. Aware of the doctor's great appetite for sweets, Miss Snowden, his black nurse at the South Side Dispensary, did a bit of plotting with her brother, a steward on the railroad. The result was a custard pie so gigantic it had to be delivered by truck and required two big men to carry it. Naturally Jacob insisted on sharing it with everyone at the Dispensary, but he happily devoured an oversized slice as well.

Coming home after one of his speeches, during which he had spoken of his love of flowers and good music, Jacob, Helen and Al found an exquisite basket of flowers and a beautifully wrapped Jascha Heifetz recording outside their apartment door.

Plants, vegetables, candies, cakes, foods of every description poured into their home, an endless river of affection for Jacob. When a patient, who was a conductor on the railroad, brought him an enormous basket of oranges from California, Jacob, overwhelmed, chided him for spending so much.

"Shucks, Doc," the conductor grinned, "it didn't cost much, but keeping the crew from taking those oranges – THAT was the real problem!"

Of all the requests for his speech, none gave him more joy and satisfaction than the invitation to address the students and faculty at his first alma mater, The Illinois School for the Blind in Jacksonville.

On November 14, 1920, as Jacob escorted Helen into the familiar chapel, memories assailed him: the frightened boy stumbling down the aisle to give his first class speech; the episode of the sixteen handkerchiefs; the joy of seeing his mother and father at his graduation.

Katie Halpin, his beloved matron, was still there.

"Miss Katie!" he exclaimed as she approached him.

"You remember me! It's been sixteen years! But you remember me!"

"Of course," Jacob replied. "I'll never forget the very first day I was here and you stopped my nosebleed and how nice it felt when you put your arms around me."

"Good! I'll do it again right now!" She enveloped Jacob in a warm hug. "I'm so proud of you. A doctor! It's incredible.

You're the only one of our graduates to become a doctor and, in all my sixteen years, the only one invited back to speak at Chapel." She turned and grasped Helen's hand. "And you're Helen, I know. I've read about you. Jake calls you his eyes."

"Helen," Jacob laughed, "this is the Katie Halpin who turned Fred and me into lifelong sinners."

"Yes, Jake," there was the bubbling, tinkling laugh Jacob remembered so well. "You called it *traif*"

"Doctor has often spoken of you," Helen said, "and all the trouble he must have caused you."

Katie caught it instantly. "Doctor! You call him Doctor and here I am calling him Jake." Her embarrassment lasted five seconds and the tinkling laugh took over. "Well, he'll always be Jake to me. No, Helen, he and Fred never caused problems, but they were so mischievous I had to keep them tied to my apron strings to keep them out of trouble. "

She removed a folded sheet of paper from her pocket. "When I learned you were coming, I thought you'd like to see your school records, but this is all I could find—your music teacher's report. This is you, Jake, when you were nine years old: *Poor memory. Slow mentally.*"

Helen's explosion of laughter joined the tinkling laugh. Jacob grinned. "I could never understand a word that teacher said."

"What a great judge of character she was!" Helen wiped tears of laughter from her eyes. "Is she still here?"

"Oh no, she's long gone. I'm the only one left from that time. Helen, you might like to know that Jake and Fred were actually the smartest boys in the whole school."

The next morning, the <u>Jacksonville Courier</u> carried the story of the triumphant return and highly inspiring speech by the school's most famous graduate.

CHAPTER 35

Jacob always referred to the month of January 1922 as the "Great Month of Letters." It began on January 3, his thirty-fourth birthday.

The Bolotins had eaten the last crumb of birthday cake. Jacob and Helen were preparing to leave for Frances Willard Hospital where he was scheduled to lecture to his evening class of doctors on diseases of the heart and lungs. As they were putting on their heavy winter overcoats, the doorbell rang.

When Al opened the door, Jacob cried out in alarm, "Harry! What brings you here at this hour? What's wrong?"

As usual, Jacob instantly recognized the visitor before a word was said.

"Everything's fine, Jake!" Judge Harry Fisher laughed, "I just wanted to be the first to congratulate you."

"Congratulate me? You mean, for my birthday?"

"I didn't know it was your birthday, but that's great! This letter I'm bringing you will be one of the best birthday gifts you ever had."

"Letter?" Helen was curious.

"I received it in the mail today and wanted to bring it to you personally."

"Please, Harry, read it to me."

"Can't, Jake. I'm on my way to a meeting, and Dave is waiting in the car in a no parking zone. A judge can't afford to get a ticket. Happy birthday, Jake. Enjoy the letter. Here, Al, read it to them."

He gave Jacob a warm bear hug, kissed Helen on the cheek and was gone.

Jacob turned to Al. "Okay, let's hear it."

Al opened the letter. "It's from the Congress of the United States House of Representatives!" he exclaimed, thoroughly awed.

185

"That's nice," Helen said. "Here, give it to me." She took the letter and began to read:

Congress of the Unites States
House of Representatives
Washington, D. C.

January 5, 1922

Hon. Harry M. Fisher,
Chicago, Ill.

Dear Judge:
I am pleased to inform you that Dr. J. W. Bolotin has been attached to the Consulting Force in the Department of Tuberculosis in the Edward Hines Jr. Hospital.

We received this information a few days ago and I know that all interested will be pleased to learn that Dr. Bolotin's services have been employed.

Sincerely yours,
H. S. Shaw
Secretary

The official notification of his appointment by the United States Health Service to the Hines Veteran's Hospital in Maywood, Illinois, arrived at his office the next morning. Jacob was elated. The position was coveted by many Chicago cardiologists and vacancies were rare. Jacob had applied months ago and, receiving no reply, assumed he had been rejected.

"You see, Al," he said with a happy grin, "it just goes to show — you must never give up hope."

The second in the "Great Month of Letters" arrived a week later. Helen, as usual, was reading Doc's mail aloud to him. Among the many requests for speeches was an invitation from Kiwanis International to be the main speaker at their upcoming national convention.

Jacob was jubilant. Helen turned away and remained silent. "Helen?"

She forced herself to speak. "It's a fine compliment," she said slowly, reluctantly.

"We must answer them immediately. Tell them I will be honored to..."

"No!" Helen slammed the letter down on the table. "You can't. Tell them no."

"What are you saying? Don't you realize what this invitation means?"

"Yes, I realize. Delegates from other states will be there."

"From every state in the Union!"

Helen refused to yield. "You're giving more speeches than you can handle now. You must begin thinking about yourself. You're exhausted. You don't have time to rest. Where will you find time for this?"

"I'll make time."

"This talk will only mean more talks. I can tell how exhausted you are even if you won't admit it. You need a rest, not another big speech..." Her voice broke. She sought refuge in Jacob's arms, pressing her face against his shoulder.

"You're right," he soothed, stroking her hair. "Of course, you're right. But you know I must do this, Helen. You know I must."

Helen knew full well it was an opportunity he could not forgo. Though every instinct screamed against it, she wrote the acceptance letter.

As Jacob spoke at the Kiwanis convention, men and women openly and unashamedly wiped tears from their eyes. After the usual standing ovation, the Kiwanians flocked to the platform with requests for the talk to be given in their own hometowns. It was not long before letters inviting him to speak to Kiwanis Clubs poured in from all over the country, but Helen again prevailed upon him to confine himself to the Midwest.

It was just as she had feared. With the demand for his speeches doubled by the torrent of requests from Kiwanis Clubs, Jacob no longer had a free moment to rest or relax.

Compelled by "the need to serve others as I have been served," he could never deny an invitation to speak and refused all fees offered him. Quietly, Helen added the reviews of his speeches to the already overflowing boxes in the dining room closet.

Gary, Indiana

> It was certainly the most inspiring speech ever heard here. Dr. Bolotin will rank with Helen Keller as one of the great blind persons in history.

Kalamazoo, Michigan

> Dramatic, indeed, was the address delivered by Dr. Jacob W. Bolotin of Chicago. A wonderful spirit of optimism envelopes him and he was able to tell of disappointments and heartaches with a laugh. He was accompanied by Mrs. Bolotin, and his reference to her as "his greatest asset" brought round after round of applause.

Columbia, Missouri

> He doesn't have eyes that see the world around him, but he has eyes that see deep into the human soul.

In June 1922, Kiwanis International invited the Bolotins to be its guests aboard the steamer Missouri for a ten-day excursion through the Great Lakes to their convention in Toronto. Helen had no objections this time. For Jacob, in addition to being the first chance he had to relax in the last few years, it would be the best trip of his lifetime.

CHAPTER 36

Jacob and Helen arranged for Al to go along on the trip, which thrilled their nephew. Jacob was appointed editor of the ship's daily newspaper, and Al was his number one copy boy. Al would get the latest news releases from the wireless room, read them to Jacob and run whatever errands were necessary. Often Jacob would print one of what he laughingly called his "Homemade Poems." He paid little attention to meter and rhyme. More important was the message each poem conveyed.

Though the delegates enjoyed teasing "Dr. Poet," they took the messages seriously, made copies to take back to their local clubs and several were later published in their monthly newspaper, Kiwanis International. Everyone's favorite was simply titled *To Kiwanis*.

To Kiwanis

Kiwanis says, "We build!"
   Kiwanians will never shirk
The blind man wants to help,
   But the public won't let him work.

It's up to you, Kiwanians,
   Don't sympathize or sob.
Just put your shoulder to the wheel
   And find the blind a job.

More than money, more than fame,
   Will be to me the day,
When every sightless, jobless man
   Will draw his first week's pay.

The first Sunday morning aboard ship, Jacob announced he wanted all the boys and girls on deck. When the curious children had assembled, he declared, "I have a surprise for you. We're going to have Sunday school."

Giggles, groans and moans greeted his pronouncement.

"Not me!" a child shouted.

"Me neither!" several sang out.

"I'd rather play ball," a tall nine-year-old stated firmly.

"All right!" Jacob's voice topped the chorus of indignant rejections. "'Let's make a bargain, okay?" The children quieted. "All I ask is ten minutes. Just try my Sunday school for ten minutes. Then, if you don't like it, we'll forget the whole idea. Is that fair enough?"

"Yep! That's fair," a tiny red-haired girl replied, her curls dancing as she nodded.

"Well, I guess that's fair." The tall boy looked around at the others. "But only ten, okay?

"Okay," the other children agreed reluctantly.

They plopped down on the deck facing Jacob, who was seated on a steel locker beside the ship's railing. He was thoroughly enjoying the challenge.

"Tell me," he said, "how many of you know the story of Joseph and His Brothers?"

A chorus of "I don'ts" and two "I dos."

"So," Jacob nodded, "only two. Then, I will tell it to the rest of you and maybe the two who know it will help me."

He began relating the Biblical story, and the ten minutes stretched to twenty. The youngsters sat entranced. Attracted by the scene, adults soon surrounded the children and listened with the same rapt attention to the ancient tale from the Old Testament.

It was a beautiful day with a blue sky and bright sun sparkling off the whitecaps on the lake. The idyllic setting, combined with Jacob's magical storytelling, was mesmerizing.

When the story ended, the deck rang with applause and Jacob grinned broadly as the children cried, "Another story! Tell us another story!"

"No," he said, rising to his feet. "It's almost time for lunch. But would you like Sunday school again next week?"

The youngsters' cheers told Jacob the challenge had been won. The Kiwanians promptly christened him the "Pied Piper" and teased him mercilessly during the remainder of the cruise.

On the second Sunday, the last aboard ship, he found his audience waiting for him. For years afterward, Jacob fondly recalled his "meteoric rise and demise" as a Sunday school teacher.

One afternoon, a group was out on deck enjoying the fresh air when Jacob suddenly pointed to the East and announced, "We're coming to an island."

"How do you know?" several asked.

"I smell it," Jacob replied.

There was such a burst of hooting and laughter that others came running to see what the fun was all about.

"Doctor Jake says he can smell an island out that way!"

"That's ridiculous!" they jeered. "Nobody can smell an island."

Everyone looked hard where Jacob pointed but saw nothing except water.

"Hey! You're kidding, right?"

"I'm betting half-a-buck he's wrong!" one skeptic shouted.

"You're on!" yelled another. "I know Jake! I'm raising you half-a-buck!"

The jovial betting became fast and lively as they lined the railing watching intently for the elusive island.

The sun was setting in the west as the dinner bell rang. People began leaving for the dining room, but Al clung to the railing because he knew his uncle was never wrong. Suddenly, far on the horizon, he saw it.

"Look! Look!" Al screamed. "The island! Look!"

Everyone turned back. Clearly visible were the twinkling lights and dim outline of land.

"Jake's right! Jake's right! Let's tell him."

Everyone started hunting for Jacob to congratulate him. A quick search found him in the dining room with Helen, serenely enjoying his T-bone steak. After that, no one ever again contested Jacob when he announced they would be passing another ship or the proximity of another island. His acute sense of smell mystified everyone. Several were positive he was psychic.

"Smell, hell" they said. "He's psychic! That's how he does it!" Jacob never contradicted them.

When the ship arrived in Toronto, he was surprised to find a reporter from the <u>Toronto Globe</u> waiting to interview him. He never understood why the reporters always sought him out over people he felt were far more important.

The next morning, several excited Kiwanians brought Jacob the early edition where he was directly quoted:

WITHOUT GIFT OF SIGHT, HE WRUNG REWARDFROM FATE AND IS NOW GREAT PHYSICIAN

Inspiring is Life-story of Dr. Bolotin Of Chicago, Blind Friend of Sick, Who Earned His Fame in Face of Handicap and Discouragements

Totally blind from his birth—and yet at the comparatively early age of thirty-four one of the most prominent consulting physicians of Chicago! Such is the amazing story of Dr. J. W. Bolotin, a visiting Kiwanian who arrived yesterday on the good ship Missouri. It is the story of courage and determination which surmounted all obstacles until he stands at the head of a profession which the average man would consider absolutely closed to the blind.

"I find much that is sweet in life, despite my handicap, and frequently forget that I am blind...I enjoy a game of

> pinochle and on the boat, enjoyed many games with other Kiwanians...I could find my way from top to bottom of the boat and fooled lots of passengers by praising the scenery... After three days association, I got to know everyone... I had a wonderful time."

There was exceptional rapport between the Kiwanians and Jacob. They accepted him as a human being, not a handicapped human being. Their camaraderie and friendship added a new dimension to his life.

With its motto, "We Build," the fraternal organization was the perfect embodiment of his own purpose in life, a purpose summed up in two words, "Help Others." Returning home, he wrote to a friend:

> *"I had such a dandy time that I became a thousand percent Kiwanian and joined the West Side Kiwanis Club."*

Jacob in 1923

It was not long before he became one of the best-known Kiwanian in the Central states. He was appointed a trustee of the club, elected Chairman of the Educational Committee of the All-Chicago Council for the year 1923, and became Lieutenant Governor Junior of the Illinois-Eastern Iowa District, Division II.

Jacob had no way of knowing his simple decision to join Kiwanis would have repercussions far beyond the city of Chicago, and would soon open up a new, exciting world filled with undreamed of opportunities for hundreds of blind boys.

CHAPTER 37

Jacob was devoted to the Chicago Lighthouse, a haven for the blind who came in search of companionship and recreation, or wished to learn a craft. Jacob came regularly to teach anatomy, Mechano-Therapy, Braille and to give them free examinations.

His arrival was always greeted with a joyous welcome. They knew he loved them as they loved him. He was their "Doctor Jake," the symbol of what the blind could achieve, the hope they so desperately needed.

A. J. [no one ever learned his last name] never missed a day. Tall, muscular, balding, he had been a successful blacksmith until an accident had left him blind and partially brain damaged. Fortunately, he possessed a broad sense of humor that sustained him and satisfied his need to be the center of attention.

A. J. adored Jacob. He always seated himself closest to the door to make certain he'd be the first to announce Doctor Jake's arrival. He would wait impatiently for the welcoming hullabaloo to subside, then challenge the learned Doctor with a riddle guaranteed to stump him. He had craftily supplied the answer to everyone there so they could all share the delicious anticipation of Jacob's puzzlement.

"Okay, Doctor Jake," he'd bellow, "I've got one for you!"

The first time it happened, the answer was obvious to Jacob. When A. J. asked, "Who does a duck see when he's sick?"

Jacob replied, "A quack doctor, of course," expecting a burst of laughter. Instead, there was a thunderous silence.

A. J. collapsed like a broken china doll. "Yep, right," he mumbled and sank back into his chair, humiliated and miserable.

Jacob never made the same mistake again. From that time on he enjoyed playing "straight-man" to A. J.'s riddles. After giving several wild guesses that elicited excited guffaws, giggles, and groans, he'd exclaim, "Okay, A. J., I give up! Why did the doctor tiptoe past the bathroom?"

"Because," A. J. gloried in the moment as he supplied the answer, "he didn't want to wake up the sleeping pills."

The hall rang with laughter and no one laughed louder than Dr. Jacob Bolotin.

On a shining July day in 1922, Jacob attended a Lighthouse picnic in Chicago's Forest Preserves with Helen and Al. Gradually they became aware of cheering and applause emanating from a nearby grove. Curious, Jacob asked Helen to find out what was causing the excitement.

"It's a troop of Boy Scouts," she informed them on her return. "They are putting on demonstrations for their parents."

"What kind of demonstrations?" Jacob asked eagerly.

"All kinds of different ones. They are drilling, building campfires, pitching tents, making things."

"Sounds like they are having a wonderful time."

"They certainly are, and so are their parents. Oh, Doctor, if only you could see how proud they are!"

The next day, Jacob went directly to the downtown Chicago headquarters of the Boy Scouts of America and was immediately ushered into the office of the Executive Director, G. N. Stephenson.

"Dr. Bolotin," he said cordially, "I have heard about you and am delighted to meet you personally. Please, sit down." He placed a chair beside Jacob.

"Sir," Jacob began without preamble, "I have come to talk with you about a matter close to my heart. I want to organize a scout troop for blind boys."

Stephenson gasped. "That's impossible!"

"Why?" Jacob asked politely. "Is a blind boy different from any other boy?"

"You are speaking of boys who cannot see."

"But that doesn't mean they can't learn. Won't you agree they have an equal right to the fun, training and opportunities scouting offers?"

"Equal right, yes, of course. But do they have equal capability? Scouting activities are based upon sight. They can't be done without..."

"Eyes? Mr. Stephenson, God gave us five senses. Eyes are only one."

"Believe me, Dr. Bolotin, I fully understand your concern, however..."

"No, you do not understand," Jacob interrupted gently. "Only a blind person can understand the miracle wrought when he discovers he can acquire the same skills as the sighted, do the same things, even accomplish his wildest dreams. Mr. Stephenson, a troop of blind boys would create many such miracles."

"You are quite persuasive, Doctor, but I still find it impossible to believe scouting can be mastered by sightless children."

Jacob smiled. "I am a doctor...and I am blind."

There was a heavy silence. Strangely unnerved, Jacob waited tensely for Stephenson's reply. When he finally spoke, his voice took on a new depth.

"Forgive me, Doctor. I am the one who is blind."

Jacob's heart leaped. "Does that mean I have permission to go ahead?"

Stephenson hesitated. "It's just that the idea is so new, so startling."

"All the more reason to try," Jacob urged.

"Perhaps, if you would work with the troop personally, if you would serve as Scoutmaster..."

"Of course! That's my intention!" Jacob sprang to his feet. "Have I your permission to proceed?"

"You have more than that, Dr. Bolotin!" Stephenson grasped Jacob's hand. "You have my promise to help in every way I can!"

So was born Troop 300, one of the first blind scout troops in the world.

Scoutmaster Bolotin was never happier than when working with "his boys." But Stephenson was almost immediately filled with misgivings. Had he allowed Dr. Bolotin's enthusiasm to create a catastrophe?

Bolotin was a doctor—he knew nothing of Scouting. The blind boys would be helpless without guidance and leadership. The Scout manual had never been printed in Braille. He decided he should attend the meetings. Jacob welcomed him warmly. He understood why Stephenson came and suggested to him that, for the next four weeks, he arrange for sighted Scouts to do their "good turn" by teaching Troop 300 the traditional Scouting crafts: knot-tying, signaling, first aid, the Morse Code. Jacob learned right along with them.

After the four sessions, Scoutmaster Bolotin took over. Applying the techniques learned at the School for the Blind in Jacksonville, he taught "his boys" to play games with balls filled with tinkling bells, to learn Braille, to hone their senses of touch, hearing and smell, to march and drill, to stand tall and walk unaided, confidently and fearlessly. They mastered all the Scouting crafts and earned their merit badges through accomplishment, not indulgence.

Jacob, with Helen and Al, often took them on picnics, outings and field trips to museums and fire stations. The boys loved the fire stations, for they were allowed to do what most boys could only dream of doing—scramble over the fire trucks while the delighted firemen answered their barrage of questions.

The troop began with seven boys and grew rapidly to twenty. It soon became apparent that permanent financial assistance was imperative if it was to survive. Jacob was determined that it would. Remembering the Scout demonstration in the park, he arranged for Troop 300 to present its own demonstration before his West Side Kiwanis Club.

The men watched with amazement as the boys drilled with the precision of West Point cadets and skillfully demonstrated their crafts. Watching the blind Scouts perform their difficult tasks with confidence and pride was a deeply emotional experience for the Kiwanians, and they listened intently to Jacob's appeal.

"Troop 300 has three goals," Jacob told them, "to help the boys develop self-reliance, to prepare for the hardships of life in a dark world and to take their places in society as worthy and useful citizens. Fellow Kiwanians," he went on, "Troop 300 needs your support. Troop 300 asks this club to become its permanent sponsor."

The Kiwanians leaped to their feet, cheering, and the future of Troop 300 was assured.

At the next meeting, the Chair rapped his gavel. "I know we're all proud that West Side Kiwanis is sponsoring, as far as we know, the first troop of blind Scouts in the world. Jacob Bolotin has completed the gigantic job of knocking out a complete seven-volume Scout handbook in Braille. The boys need uniforms. What are we going to do about it?"

Arms shot up.

"I move we dig into the kitty and outfit everyone of the kids!"

"Do I have a second?"

"Second! Second! Second!" The men shouted almost in unison.

The Kiwanians took their sponsorship seriously. They not only purchased uniforms, they chauffeured the boys to meetings and sponsored two-week stays at the Boy Scout summer Camp Owasippee in Michigan.

Here the boys learned to swim and hike, to pitch a tent and build a campfire, and something no sighted boy could do – identify a tree, not only by odor, but by simply holding a leaf in his hand.

At the end of the two weeks, Troop 300 presented its demonstration. It created such a sensation, Stephenson arranged for the presentation at the big Boy Scout Jamboree that fall. As a result, Troop 300 was kept busy performing at school assemblies, conventions and between innings at intramural ball games.

Stephenson seldom missed a demonstration and never ceased being thrilled as he watched the troop thank the audience with a crisp salute, a sharp turn, and march proudly out in perfect formation as the applause and cheers rang in their ears.

"It's incredible," Stephenson said to Helen after a demonstration in a ballpark. "I admit I was very skeptical. I was so certain a troop of blind boys would be a catastrophe. But, you know what's really funny? The other troops are jealous and are working harder than ever before." He paused, then added slowly, "I'll never forget what Dr. Bolotin said the first time we met. 'Only a blind person,' he said, 'can understand the miracle wrought when he learns he can do the same things a sighted person does. A troop of blind boys would create many such miracles.' He was right. Troop 300 is not a catastrophe. Troop 300 is a miracle."

The reporter for the Chicago Tribune agreed with him:

> Though neither their leader nor the boys have ever seen each other, Dr. Bolotin developed the troop into one of the best in the organization performing most of the feats accomplished by more fortunate boys in other troops.

CHAPTER 38

At eight o'clock on a June night in 1923, Chicago was still simmering from the stifling heat reflected from the streets, sidewalks and brick buildings that had baked since early morning in the merciless sun. All the windows in the Bolotins' apartment were open to catch even a hint of cooling breezes.

Helen, Jacob and Al had just finished supper. Al was helping Helen clear the dishes when she put her hand on his arm and nodded her head towards Jacob. They were both worried. Instead of the usual lively mealtime discussions, Jacob had been strangely silent. His face pale and drawn with fatigue, he remained slumped back in his chair and made no attempt to retire to his big leather chair in the sun parlor as he usually did. Helen bit her lip as she watched him intently for a long moment. Then she walked behind him and slid her arms around his shoulders.

"Darling," her voice was soft and dreamy, "remember how we used to take long rides on Saturdays, attend a concert or an opera in the evening, hike on the beach on Sundays? Wouldn't it be wonderful to do that again?"

"Yes," Jacob smiled. "It would be wonderful, but you're forgetting something, Helen. That was before I was loaded with classes and patients and speeches."

'That's it, Doctor! That's exactly it! You don't have the strength for all that anymore. Cancel half your teaching load, cut down your patient load, stop running to all the clinics and dispensaries and sanitariums..."

"What are you saying, Helen? Those are my jobs. I have to earn a living. Santa Claus brings toys, he doesn't pay bills. Be reasonable, Helen. Think! Think!"

"I am thinking! I'm thinking of all the hours you squeeze out volunteering at the prisons."

"I'm helping the men. Besides," Jacob shrugged, "it's only five hours a week."

"But those are hours you could be resting. I'm thinking of the hours you give up to teach a class of dentists. For God's sake, you're not a dentist."

"They asked me to."

"You could say no!"

"They need to learn how to recognize heart problems."

"Good! Someone else can teach them! I'm thinking of every Saturday afternoon at the Lighthouse. That can be cut to two Saturdays, or even one a month. Then," she giggled, "A. J. wouldn't need all those riddles."

"No," Jacob mused, "he'd be very disappointed."

"But you'd have time for rest." She leaned forward and kissed the top of his head. "Oh, it's very altruistic giving up every free hour to volunteering and speeches, but they don't pay bills. They only rob you of precious hours of rest. You haven't regained your strength since the influenza epidemic. It was a miracle you didn't collapse then. You haven't been yourself in a long time. What good will you be to anybody if you break down now? Please, you must give yourself at least one day a week for rest. You know, darling," she tried to mask her concern with light banter, "even God rested on the seventh day."

Jacob heard the tension, the fear, beneath her words. He tried to laugh it off.

"Yes," he teased, "God had to. He had a big job. He created the heavens and the earth. I didn't."

"No!" Helen fired back, "you didn't create them, but you're trying to change the whole earth all by yourself." She broke away from Doc, walked around the table and turned to face him. "You've become a Crusader! You've assigned yourself the holy cause of alerting the world to the problems of the handicapped. All you need is a coat of armor and a spear so you can rescue the underprivileged."

"Helen! Please understand."

"No! You understand! Every speech you give brings requests for ten more. To you, that means ten more chances to get your message out, and you never say no."

"I never will. You know that. It has to be done!"

"But the world isn't ready for all that. People are busy with their own lives. They don't care!"

"I don't believe that! People don't care because they don't know. Nobody ever told them. That's why I've got to. I'm only thirty-four; maybe by the time I'm forty-five there will even be laws protecting the handicapped."

"Forty-five!" Helen was a cloud of fury. "You won't even make forty the way you're driving yourself. You're Don Quixote tilting at windmills. All you're accomplishing is exhausting yourself."

"Maybe so, but Don Quixote never gave up, and neither will I."

"But you can't do it alone. Don't you realize you're giving a speech somewhere every night in the week and sometimes three and four in a day? You can't keep on going like that."

"Maybe, someday," Doc's voice was vibrant with hope, "there will be many other voices raised. But right now, there's only one other person, Helen Keller. We talk about it every time we share a speaker's platform. She's trying hard."

"Well, bully for her! She isn't tied down with patients and teaching, and hospitals, and sanitariums. She's free to talk about it everywhere she goes. You can't."

"I can at least lecture whenever and wherever I'm asked. I'll never say no! Never!"

Helen knew what she demanded was unthinkable to Jacob. Still she fought on.

"Your schedule is impossible!"

"Please, Helen! I know what my schedule is."

"Do you? There's not another doctor in this city who carries an eighteen hour schedule seven days a week."

"Yes, it's heavy. I worked like a maniac to achieve it. And I'm proud of it, proud of what it proves."

"What?" Helen struggled for self-control. "What does it prove, except that it's killing you?"

"It proves — and you of all people should understand — that a blind man can be as wanted, as useful in this sighted world as anybody else."

"You have proven it! A thousand times over! Now you think, Doctor. You think! You're not only teaching students at three universities, you're teaching nurses, and good heaven," she clapped her hand to her forehead, "you're teaching doctors! How long must you go on proving it? No! Your trouble is you can't stop proving it. You can't stop giving of yourself!" Helen's voice was edged with hysteria. She knew she was fighting for Jacob's life. "But no more!" she cried. "No more! You're so tired, you can't sleep nights. I know you're in pain all the time. You never say anything, but I'm not blind! I see it! I've always done what you asked, gone along with everything you wanted. But no more! Now you will listen to me! You will start saying no!" Her words, blurred by tears, she made one last futile effort. "At least," she begged, "at least, let someone else take over the Scout troop."

Gently, Jacob gathered her into his arms and held her close until she quieted. Then he said slowly, "Helen, you're asking me to break a promise, my promise to Stephenson that I'd serve as Scoutmaster. I asked for that responsibility."

"Responsibility?" Helen echoed wearily, her voice threaded with defeat, "Your only responsibility is to your family. To me—I love you. To Al—he's the son you've always wanted. You're the father he never had. Don't you understand? We love you. We don't want to lose you." Her voice thinned away to a whisper, "We don't want to lose you."

"Stop worrying," Jacob soothed softly. "I'm a little tired tonight, that's all. I'll feel better tomorrow."

In fact, Jacob's health had been taxed beyond its endurance, and he was on the verge of collapse. Overwork finally took its toll.

CHAPTER 39

A few weeks later Jacob became seriously ill and was confined to bed. The news of his illness spread rapidly. Helen found herself coping with a flood of cards, letters, flowers, gifts of food, plus an endless procession of visitors. Doctors called asking for the privilege of attending to him. Finally Helen accepted the offers of two of Chicago's finest physicians, James Herrick and Sidney Kuh.

"We would be greatly honored," they told Helen, "if you would permit us to attend to Dr. Bolotin."

Helen decided to say nothing to Jacob to diminish his surprise when the doctors would walk in. They arrived that same afternoon, and Helen led them into Jacob's room, where he lay half asleep.

"You have visitors," she said.

Jacob turned and tried to sit up as Herrick grasped his hand.

"Hello, Jake," he said.

"Jim! Jim Herrick!" Jacob gasped.

"Hello, Jake," Kuh said.

"Sid! Sid Kuh!" Jacob was stunned. Helen enjoyed the silent byplay between the two men as they exchanged amazed glances.

"How did you know it was us?" Herrick asked. "All we said was hello."

"It was enough," Jacob teased. "Can't mistake your operatic baritones. Now, why are you two busy guys wasting time here?"

"Well," Kuh laughed lightly, "since your classes for doctors were temporarily called off we decided this is the perfect time to test some of the techniques you taught us."

"And," Herrick added, "we'd never find a more perfect patient to test them on."

"Getting back at me, are you?" Jacob laughed, "Okay, boys, go at it. I'm all yours."

"Fingertips and ears, Jim," Kuh reminded Herrick. "Remember Jake's mantra—fingertips and ears."

"Right, boys," Jacob grinned as he unbuttoned his pajama top. "Let's see how much you've learned. First, your stethoscopes."

Each examined him carefully with his stethoscope.

"Okay, now your ear. Close your eyes and concentrate..."

Each placed his ear upon Doc's bare chest and listened intently. Jacob waited.

"Hear anything else?"

"No," Herrick admitted awkwardly.

"Sid?"

"I don't know," Kuh replied. "I thought I detected a kind of—I don't know how to describe it—but there was something more."

"Good," Jacob smiled happily. "Sid, you're improving— you get a C. Jim, you flunked."

Helen's laughter camouflaged her heartache. Here Jacob lay, sick and weak, still teaching, still trying, and offering his own body as a learning tool.

The two men were well aware that Jacob, with his practiced fingers searching his body, knew his condition far better than they did. His heart was struggling to keep up with the strain that Jacob had put on it. They prescribed bed rest and they came regularly to examine him.

Jacob improved very slowly, but, impatient as always, announced he was ready to go back to work after only a month. Worried, the two doctors warned Helen it was imperative for him to have at least several more months of complete rest before they would permit him to resume his activities.

She immediately rented two rooms with a sleeping porch in a heavily wooded section of Lake Forest, a North Shore suburb.

"There are no people here," Helen reported to Dr. Herrick, "but with the trees, the birds and all the little wild creatures about us, it is very noisy. Doctor loves the noise. He spends hours every day just listening to the wonderful sounds."

Jacob enjoyed the singing but, unable to put aside his concern for his patients, he insisted on traveling to the city once a week to make house calls. Helen was able to keep him from resuming his other duties, but he was adamant about taking care of his patients. Perhaps he knew he had only a short time to live. Even though he never spoke of it, Jacob was obsessed with the need to use every living hour to its fullest. Rest, to Jacob, was time wasted. As he grew stronger, he refused to tolerate his imposed isolation any longer.

"I've had enough," he said to Helen. "I'm not staying here another day."

"We can't go home yet. Herrick and Kuh want you to have at least another month."

"Month!" Jacob exploded. "I'll go crazy! Besides, I feel great! I'm fine!"

"Then just one more week," Helen pleaded, "while the fall weather is so beautiful."

"Not another day! I've wasted too many days of my life doing nothing. No! Not one more day!"

Helen knew when he made up his mind it was useless to argue. They returned home, and he happily threw himself headlong into his full roster of duties and speeches.

CHAPTER 40

The demands on Jacob were staggering, yet in spite of his weakened health he always found time to do more. He was now the Chief Tuberculosis Specialist of Hines Veterans Hospital; head of the tuberculosis ward at the Chicago House of Corrections; clinical consultant for the Livingston County Tuberculosis Sanitarium in Pontiac, Illinois, as well as for the Highland-LaSalle Tuberculosis Sanitarium in Ottowa, Illinois; Chair of Diagnosis in three universities; conducting classes for nurses and doctors at Willard Hospital; continuing his duties at the Municipal Tuberculosis Clinics, while conscientiously making house calls and maintaining office hours to treat the avalanche of patients clamoring to see him.

And the speeches. He was obsessed with the need to spread his pleas for the handicapped and the underprivileged to the world. It didn't matter to him how large or small his audience was. He spoke wherever he was invited. Each person there represented a chance to reach two or three or four more so that his message would spread far beyond the immediate perimeter of his voice.

In Monroe, Wisconsin, on December 8, 1923, Jacob was scheduled to speak at a Kiwanis Club luncheon, a high school assembly in the afternoon, and to deliver his address on "A Square Deal for the Underprivileged Child" in the evening. It was a speech he had introduced a year earlier and was remarkable for its compassion and insight into the crushing problems of the poor and underprivileged. Grounded in his own intimate experience with poverty and affliction, the speech was an impassioned plea for help from the more fortunate. It had become one of his most requested talks. [Please see the Appendix for the text of this speech.]

Jacob immediately saw the hours between speeches as an

opportunity to raise funds for these children by offering free examinations.

Covering the unusual event, the newspaper reporter wrote:

22 PEOPLE ARE ALREADY ON THE LIST FOR THURSDAY AFTERNOON AND ON FRIDAY MORNING, DR. BOLOTIN WILL EXAMINE AS MANY AS POSSIBLE UNTIL 1 O'CLOCK TRAIN TIME BACK TO CHICAGO

Dr. Bolotin gives his expert advice free of charge and will lecture at Turner Hall for the same fee tonight – nothing. He does it because it is a cause near his heart, because he had a hard row to hoe in his young days and now that he doesn't have to scratch and scrape for every dime in order to eat or further his education, he believes in helping those who can use his aid. He receives a fee of $25.00 for an examination in his Chicago office that he is giving to people of this community for nothing.

The doctor hopes many who are examined, and are able to, will donate to a fund which is the object of the proceeds from his lecture tonight. The fund is dispensed by the Kiwanis Club in aid to the underprivileged child. There were four children found in the morning examination who will benefit from the fund created by his lecture, their medical fees for the treatment recommended by Dr. Bolotin, being paid from this fund as far as it will go. Every 50¢ "tossed into the hat" at the hall tonight, will go to aid some afflicted child that otherwise would

not have that aid. It cannot but help that
child and possibly save a life, making it a
truly noble effort.

Dr. Bolotin appeared here some three
months ago for a lecture. So impressive
was his story, his congenial, happy,
inspiring nature, that since then he has
been in great demand for similar talks
before Kiwanis Clubs in the Middle West.
The vice president of the international
organization states Dr. Bolotin is today
recognized throughout the organization
among the first and best known of the
hundreds of thousands of members,
through the good work he is doing.

To those who did not know him, Jacob's enthusiasm and
good spirits hid his weakening health. His family and close
friends knew he was very ill. This was to be his last speech.

CHAPTER 41

In January Jacob celebrated his thirty-sixth birthday with his family. They all feared it would be his last. He was sick once again.

On February 11, 1924, he wrote to a friend:

> *"My illness has taken a downward course, and my doctors have ordered me to bed for several weeks to avoid a general nervous collapse. Though it smashes all my business and plans to thunder, I am taking my medicine without a grumble."*

But he did grumble when he was unable to present a radio talk requested by the Boy Scouts of America for February 28 at the request of his good friend, Stephenson.

He grew perceptibly weaker as the days passed. He was aware his kidneys were failing as well as his heart. Yet, his rapier wit and good humor remained undimmed, and his buoyant optimism sustained the family.

Every morning, Hookway came to sit beside Jacob and the two men would debate and discuss as they always had. Though Jacob tried to keep up the animated pace they both loved, he tired quickly and became increasingly content to lie back and allow Hookway to do the talking.

The prolonged illness, which had abruptly ended Jacob's income, was a heavy financial burden upon the Bolotins. Jacob was stubborn about money. He had always refused to discuss finances or accept loans. Worried, Hookway cast about for some way to help.

He arrived as usual one morning while Al was reading the paper to Jacob. After they had chatted for some time about some current events, Hookway said lightly, "By the way, I just sold that lot I've been trying to get rid of all these years. Got seven thousand dollars." He laughed. "Now that I have all that money, I don't know what to do with it."

"You'll find some use for it," Jacob replied.

"Sure don't know what I'll ever do with it," Hookway said thoughtfully. "Of course!" he slapped his knee gleefully. "I know how to use it! I'll deposit it to your account." The idea sounded convincingly sudden. "Think I'll do it right now. See you tomorrow, Doc."

As he started to rise, Jacob reached out to stop his old friend. He tried to speak, but could only shake his head.

"Doesn't matter," Hookway seemed unconcerned. "I can do it tomorrow as well."

"No," Jacob's voice was choked, his words firm, "you won't do it at all."

"Look, Doc," Hookway persisted, "I don't need the money. It's just sitting there in the bank."

"It's good of you to offer." Jacob tightened his grip on Hookway's knee. "Thank you for that. But I can't accept."

"Damn it, Doc! Why not use it?"

"It would be impossible for Helen to repay."

"She wouldn't have to."

"No, it's out of the question." Jacob paused. Then he began to chuckle. "Hookway, you devil, I don't need eyes to see right through you. How long have you been plotting this?"

"Well," Hookway admitted sheepishly, "for a while."

They broke into laughter to cover the intensity of their emotions, and Hookway knew the subject was closed.

Even as his own life was fading, Jacob was constantly taking care of others. Al would regularly hurry home from school to read to Jacob. One day he said, "Sit beside me, Al. I want to talk to you." He reached for the boy's hand and held it for a few minutes before he spoke. "You have a heart murmur but with proper care you can live a long time, longer than any of us. Just remember, don't overdo. There's always another streetcar, another chance."

He fell silent, and Al was grateful that Jacob could not see his face as he fought for control. It was the last time Al ever saw him alone.

CHAPTER 42

The next day, Dr. Kuh arranged for Jacob to be taken to the North Shore Health Resort in Winnetka, a suburb on the shore of his beloved Lake Michigan. He was allowed no visitors. When Al was told that he would not be permitted to see Jacob either, he was desolate.

"I'm family," Al argued, but it was useless.

Finally, using the resourcefulness he had learned from his uncle, Al took the train to Winnetka and walked into the hospital hoping to slip unnoticed into Jacob's room. Helen stopped him.

"You should not have come," she said angrily.

"I want to see Doc. Just for a minute," Al begged.

"No. He's very sick. You know his doctor said no visitors."

"Then I won't visit. I'll only look at him. Aunt Helen, please let me just look at him."

"All right," she agreed reluctantly, "but just from the doorway. He will recognize you if you come any closer. And don't make a sound."

Jacob was lying propped up on pillows. Al saw that face was emaciated, drawn with pain. His skin looked gray against the white linens. He lay limp with no trace of his ebullient, buoyant spirit. Al had a clear premonition that he would never again see Jacob alive. He slumped against the door.

Jacob's private nurse, Mary Honan, sitting beside the bed, had been watching Al closely. Seeing his anguish, she rose and motioned for Al to follow her down the hall. When they were safely out of Jacob's hearing, she asked, "Are you Al?"

He nodded numbly.

"The Doctor has asked about you many times. It'll please him to know you were here. I'll tell him." Her eyes were brimming with compassion. "He loves you very much."

Jacob's condition continued to worsen. Unable to reach Dr. Kuh or Dr. Herrick, who was vacationing in Europe, in desperation Helen telephoned Dr. Babcock, though she was well aware of Jacob's implacable hatred for the man. For sixteen years, since the ill-fated meeting in Babcock's office, Jacob had never mentioned his name again. She shuddered as she faced the task of telling him what she had done.

"No!" Jacob shouted. "Not Babcock!"

"He is coming," Helen said. "He's on the way."

"I won't have him! Anybody but Babcock! Send him back!"

Helen had foreseen her husband's anger, but she was completely taken aback by the intensity of his fury. Fearing the effect of the emotional attack upon his weakened body, she rushed to the lobby to warn Babcock. When he arrived in his chauffeured limousine, she accosted him breathlessly.

"Dr. Babcock, thank you for coming, but my husband will not permit you to examine him."

Babcock smiled affably. "I expected that, Mrs. Bolotin. But I am going to see him."

"No, no! Please! You can't! He's too emotional, too agitated."

"Of course, I understand. But seeing Dr. Bolotin is something I must do...something I've waited many years to do."

"I'm frightened for him, Doctor."

"Please, Mrs. Bolotin, trust me."

Confused, troubled, Helen led Babcock to Jacob's room. He paused at the door, then, with an almost imperceptible squaring of his shoulders, he approached the bed.

"Dr. Bolotin, I am Dr. Babcock"

Helen waited tensely for Jacob's reply. His words came slowly, smoothly masking his fury.

"I remember your voice as I remember your advice."

"It was bad advice."

"I got along without your help then. I do not want your help now."

"I don't blame you for feeling the way you do. For years I've regretted my rudeness, my lack of courtesy."

Helen caught her breath. Would Jacob accept the apology?

"I appreciate your courtesy in coming now," Jacob's voice was supremely polite, "but I do not need your services."

Babcock hesitated. He chose his words carefully.

"Permit me to tell you why I spoke as I did when you came to my office. I thought I was saving you from disappointment, from certain failure. You wanted to achieve something far beyond you."

"You did not know me."

"No, but I knew myself. I had my eyes while I was young; you were born blind. I was wealthy; you were penniless. I had tutors, servants, a chauffeured car, everything I needed. You had nothing."

"I had my ambition! My dream!"

"Yes, a dream too many sighted students fail to achieve. It seemed impossible. I tried to stop you."

"You failed."

"I'm glad I failed. I have followed your career with intense interest and admiration. In these few years, you have accomplished great things," his voice grew wistful, "far more than I have, and I am twice your age."

"We could have been friends," Jacob murmured, his words barely audible.

Helen's heart leaped as she saw Jacob's hand rise slowly, groping for Babcock. Quickly, she grasped Babcock's arm and guided it forward. The two blind physicians clasped hands.

Her emotions threatening her self-control, Helen fled to the room she had taken adjoining Jacob's. Once inside, the pent up agonies of the past months, released by the scene she had just witnessed, exploded into a sea of tears. She wept convulsively for several minutes, then, grateful that neither man could see her tear-stained face, she went back to Jacob's room.

Babcock, his examination completed, replaced his stethoscope in his bag.

"It was good of you to come," Jacob said warmly.

'I'm honored that your wife called me. I will see you again in two days."

"Goodbye, Dr. Babcock."

Helen was startled by the note of finality in Jacob's voice. Turning, she led Babcock to the lobby.

"Doctor," she said, "I cannot thank you enough for coming to see my husband."

"No, Mrs. Bolotin, it's I who thank you for giving me that privilege. I wish there was more I could do to help him now, but... In any case, I will look in on him again day after tomorrow."

"I will send you a check immediately. What is your fee?"

Babcock smiled. "There is no fee, Mrs. Bolotin." He placed his hand on her shoulder. "Your husband would have done the same for me."

The next morning, Dr. Cheney, medical director of the hospital, making his morning rounds, greeted Jacob with his customary joviality.

"How are you, Dr. Bolotin? You look fine."

Jacob had always responded with a jest. Now he was angry.

"I know my condition all too well. I'm not afraid to die. I have a brother and sister...all three of us were born blind. We have suffered hell on this earth..." His voice trailed off into silence.

It was the first time in his life be had spoken of suffering. No one had ever before heard him utter a single complaint. Only now, his indomitable spirit conquered by approaching death, too weakened to fight or resist any longer, did he finally reveal his anger at the physical punishment, the daily agonies he had endured.

That night a good friend of Helen's, Belle Blau, came to stay and watch Jacob to give Helen some time to rest. Believing Jacob asleep, she tiptoed into the room and sat down beside the door, as far from the bed as the room allowed. Since he was not to know she was there, she sat silent and unmoving. Suddenly, turning his head in her direction, Jacob said, "Belle, please give me a glass of water."

She rose quickly and brought him the water. Jacob drank slowly, seeming to savor every mouthful. Then he said quietly, "In five minutes, I will be dead."

Belle raced, panic-stricken, to get Helen and Nurse Honan. As they surrounded his bed, he admonished them softly, "Don't be afraid. I'm not afraid. I'm going to my mother." He was breathing heavily. "Helen," he tried to lift his head, "how are my boys? Who is taking care of my troop?"

Gently Helen lowered his head to the pillow. "They're fine, dear." She ran her fingers through his hair. "Some of your club members are working with them, and Fred is working with them too. Now your boys have many Scoutmasters."

"Good. Fred understands. He won't let the troop die. The Kiwanis must keep it going. You've got to tell them, Helen."

"I will. I promise. Now try to rest."

"Yes," Jacob smiled happily, "I'm going to have a long rest." He lapsed into silence, then suddenly, urgently, he exclaimed, "The funeral! It will be expensive. Helen, have we got the money?"

Nurse Honan snatched a five-dollar bill from her pocket and pushed it into Jacob's hand. He subsided.

"That's good, Helen. You'll be all right. And you mustn't be afraid. It's beautiful."

All at once, like sunlight bursting through fog, a startling change came over Jacob. The lines etched into his face by the long months of suffering seemed to vanish. He was radiant, suffused with an inner glow.

"It's exciting," he murmured, gave a soft sigh and was gone.

CHAPTER 43

It was April 1, 1924. Just twelve years after graduating from medical school, his valiant struggle against almost insurmountable obstacles had ended.

Jacob Bolotin died as he had lived, joyously, exuberantly. Just as each day had been for him a new miracle to be experienced in its full glory, death was but a new adventure to be met courageously, head on.

Five thousand people attended the funeral as Chicago poured out its love for the young doctor.

They were all there: famous and unknown, rich and poor, black and white. From the State Senators, Mayor and City Aldermen to the cronies of Herman's saloon who had banged their beer mugs on the tables and yelled, "Hey Jake! Draw me a glass!"

From university presidents, faculties, fellow students, and his own students from three universities, to Kurt Heiner, who had never forgotten the angry boy who had fought for his basket of matches.

From his medical colleagues from the clinics, dispensaries, sanitariums, hospitals, and innumerable consultations; his thousands of patients, over fifty percent of whom never knew he was blind to Sven Larsen, who had finally learned his stubborn tenant was, indeed, a "real" doctor.

The Lighthouse people came en masse, as did the seventeen-year-old teenager, now a mother of two children, whose life had been saved by a defiant young intern. Doctor Copeland, heroically camouflaging the depth of his grief, told of the determined student who had refused to accept the impossible and whose miraculous achievement had opened the eyes, minds and hearts of the entire faculty and ultimately of the medical world. Professor Bamberger told of the four-year-old who couldn't wait to start school, of the bully on the train who had taught Jacob that achievement lay only by using his mind, not his fists. Kiwanians came from all over the United States. The Kiwanis Bulletin carried a front-page story:

ILLINOIS-EASTERN IOWA DISTRICT BULLETIN
"We Build"

1924 Convention City
GALESBURG, ILLINOIS

1924 District Slogan
EVERY MEMBER CO-OPERATING

C. Asa Phelps, Editor, Marion Newton, Associate Editor. 6306 Cottage Grove Ave., Chicago

Vol. 1   APRIL, 1924   No. 2

A GREAT LOSS
By Dr. N. P. Lloyd

DR. JACOB BOLOTIN
Born January 1, 1888;
died April 1, 1924

On April 1st, our own Dr. Bolotin reached the climax of his life of service and "went over the top in darkness," but to a realization of the light that had spurred him on through the years. We who had the honor to know him grew to love him. He gave much of his valuable time appearing before Clubs of several states delivering his famous lecture *Over the Top in Darkness* without charge or fee. Many of the Clubs were visited at a time when he should have been thinking of his own physical condition, but the true Kiwanis Spirit of this great man never let him think in terms of self, but always for others.

Born blind and working his way up through handicaps which would have defeated a weaker soul, that endless courage of his overcame all until he became an expert on heart and lung disorders.

A few months ago, he started the organization of a Boy Scout troop consisting wholly of blind boys, spon-

sored by the West Side Club. Troop 300 was one of the
things nearest and dearest to his heart, and the Club
has pledged itself to carry on the noble work as a
memorial to Doctor.

One of the most touching talks I ever heard Doctor
make was on the occasion the blind boys were guests
of the Club. This was the last meeting he was able to
attend. He was not physically able to be at that meeting, yet he was there and told of the dreams he had and
things he hoped to do for these boys. He pleaded for
our support in helping them to better fit themselves for
the hardships of life, to teach them how to work, to
teach them how to play, how to smile, how to become
worthy and useful citizens. In this work, as in his
everyday life, he gave of his time, his money and his
energy in the hopes that when his time came to depart,
the world would have been benefited by his short
sojourn on earth. Can any man do more?

His genial smile, his hearty handshake, his voice
and his great heart are gone from us. No great monu-
ment may ever be erected to his memory, but the lesson of service he taught us will go on until the day the
world shall see—what he did not need eyes to see—
that service is the keynote to greatness and simplicity
the heart of truth.

May the Great Spirit instill in the minds and hearts
of the many who called him friend to "Go thou and do
likewise."

Over one thousand blind people came to say their personal
goodbyes to the man whose life was the shining symbol of
achievement that made their own dreams possible.

Hookway, Herman Friedman, Herman Woehlck, Adolph
Van Teslaar, Einar Camfield and G. N. Stephenson served as
pallbearers.

Three hundred Boy Scouts assisted in carrying the mountain of floral tributes and helped the extra policemen assigned

to keeping the hearse and mile of cars moving smoothly. Jacob's own Troop 300 served as honor guard, and the floral spray the blind boys had designed and made themselves rested atop the casket.

The reporter from the Chicago Herald and Examiner, obviously deeply moved by the ceremony, wrote:

> Soft and low, tremulous as when one chants a prayer, the voice of the blind Boy Scout was wafted above the sea of sightless, upturned faces.
>
> "Lead, kindly Light, amid the encircling gloom, Lead Thou me on."
>
> And the faces which a moment before had registered blank despair, lightened with hope and spiritual serenity. It was as if the light that had guided Dr. Jacob Bolotin for thirty-six years had reached out to shed its lustrous beams into their world of perpetual night.
>
> It was as if their beloved comrade, counselor and good minister, as they called him, had spoken to them from beyond the grave. It was as if his indomitable spirit had triumphed over death as it had over the cruel handicaps of life.
>
> There were a thousand of them there—men, women and children—doomed to a lifelong night. There were five hundred members of the Society for the Blind, scores from kindred organizations. They filled Independence Chapel, at 3165 Ogden Avenue, to overflowing. For two blocks they waited in line while services were in progress.
>
> Altogether, more than five thousand persons attended the funeral.

Rabbi Saul Silber, who had known Dr. Bolotin from boyhood, when he peddled matches to educate himself, officiated at chapel services. He spoke of the noted heart and lung specialist's achievements in the domain of medicine and of his work among the city's poor. He told how he sacrificed his life on the altar of devotion to the needy and the sick.

Michael Zimmer, warden of the Cook County Hospital, in which Dr. Bolotin contributed much of his time, eulogized him for his humanitarian ideals and high integrity. Members of various Kiwanis Clubs also spoke.

And when the speakers had finished, the procession of the blind began past the flower-banked bier. Led by relatives and friends, one by one they walked up to the casket, turned their sightless eyes upon the face of their idolized leader and went on, faces wet with tears.

At Waldheim Cemetery in Forest Park, as the family surrounded the casket, Rabbi Silber gave Professor Bamberger the honor of reciting Kaddish, the ancient Hebrew prayer for the dead. As he began the traditional words, his voice choked with sobs. He stood helpless, unable to continue. Immediately, Herman Friedman and Adolf Van Teslaar put their arms around him, and together, Jacob's three most beloved friends completed the beautiful prayer.

Many of the miraculous aids for the disabled and the laws prohibiting job discriminations that are taken for granted today began with the voice of Dr. Jacob Bolotin. His tireless, dogged push through the jungle of public ignorance and indifference paved the way for many others. As a journalist from the Philadelphia Inquirer wrote:

There is no doubt about Doctor Bolotin's buoyant optimism. His friends declare he is one of the cheeriest, lightest hearted and most genuinely happy of men—a man full of the joy of mere living.

His blindness is no tragedy to him. He regards it rather as a spur to the best that is in him. He seems to forget his infinity in his enthusiasm for his work and in his determination to succeed—not because of his blindness, but in spite of it.

Perhaps the most touching tribute, among the sacks of mail from all over the world that deluged the family's apartment after Jacob's death, was a letter from a former patient who maintained a modest tailoring shop:

"He was a wonder,

and wonders don't last"

EPILOGUE

Helen Bolotin never remarried after Dr. Bolotin's death; she sold her harp and furniture and moved back into her mother's flat. Highly respected for her expertise acquired as her husband's assistant, she was in constant demand by hospitals and doctors throughout Chicago. In 1978, she died in a nursing home at the age of 98

Alfred Perlman had planned to become a doctor, but Jacob's death six months after Al entered high school, completely changed his life. His graduation in 1927 was followed by the great economic crash of 1929, and the entire country was plunged into a devastating depression.

Determined to acquire a profession, Al began working the midnight shift at the Post Office while attending daytime classes at De Paul University. Five years later, in 1936, he received his MA in education. In 1938, a brief ceremony united Alfred and Rosalind. Several years of teaching were interrupted by nearly four years in Europe serving in the Army quartermaster corps during World War ll. Returning to Chicago in 1945, the United States Civil Service assigned him to supervise the dispersal of funds for the G.I. Bill of Rights. In 1950, the young couple moved to Santa Maria, California, where Al joined the faculty of Santa Maria High School. A heart attack forced early retirement in 1969, but did not prevent him from enjoying busy and highly satisfying years devoted to world travel and community service. He died at the age of 92 on March 6, 2001.

Herman Friedman opened an office in Rock Island, Illinois, and brought his wife and five children to the United States.

Herman Woehlck became the industrial surgeon for the Western Electric Company in Maywood, a Chicago suburb. He enjoyed a large family and a busy life before his death at age 79.

Adolph Van Teslaar married the daughter of Angela Viorin, the secretary to Romania's Prime Minister.

Einar Camfield opened an office in Lansing, Michigan.

Fred Bolotin's janitorial supply shop in Austin, a Chicago suburb, grew rapidly. Fred took over as Scoutmaster of Boy Scouts troop 300 after Jacob died and remained involved for nearly 30 years. After his death at the age of 57, his business was taken over by cousins Bernard and Hetty, moved to River Forest, Illinois, and renamed Bolotin, Inc., where it grew into one of the busiest supply centers in the Chicago area.

The Chicago College of Medicine and Surgery became the medical arm for Loyola University in 1918

Boy Scouts Troop 300 continued until 1952, when it was dissolved. More than 300 boys were members of the troop during its existence, many of whom went on to successful careers in such diverse fields as law, music and precision equipment manufacturing.

APPENDIX

"A Square Deal For the Underprivileged Child"
Presented by Dr. Jacob Bolotin on November 16, 1922
Kiwanis Club in Monroe, Wisconsin

"Every child, regardless of the state of the family finances, is entitled to the healthy, happy, normal childhood that is the birthright of every human being. By a normal childhood, I mean one in which there is proper food, adequate play, sufficient shelter, good clothing and opportunity for education.

"The hungry child is an underprivileged child. If the father doesn't earn enough to feed his family, they should not go hungry. Civic organizations not clarity should offer help. Charity only undermines pride and diminishes character."

Lamenting the lack of importance given to nutrition by physicians and educators, he advocated the establishment of classes in nutrition in medical schools as well as classes for teenagers and mothers.

"The child without opportunity for normal play is an underprivileged child." He urged that the playground movement, then in its infancy, be expanded for all children, especially for those with only city streets to play in.

"Shabby clothes mold a shabby character. To engender pride and self-respect, we must obtain new clothes for distribution among the poor, rather than the cast off garments we usually give them. "

Troubled by the tremendous increase in tuberculosis, he condemned congested tenements and stuffy parlors of that day and pleaded for more sunshine, fresh air and outdoor living.

"As there are individual differences in abilities and skills, so are there individual differences in health needs. Not only parents, but also doctors and schools have an obligation to contribute to the health consciousness and good health habits of all children. We must also have more rigid, more frequent, more thorough health inspections.

"There is no such thing, as a lazy child. It is just not natural. An investigation will invariably prove the lazy child is suffering from some form of ailment, physical or emotional.

"Being an underprivileged child comes in many variations. When a child comes to a parent with a question and is told 'don't bother me now, I'm busy,' or is given a command to do something 'because I told you to,' that is an underprivileged child. The multimillionaire's child that is being brought up by a nanny, or governess, because his parents are busy with their own lives, is as underprivileged as the impoverished child without shoes.

"The parent is the responsible trustee of a child's potential and must provide the maximum opportunities for the unfolding of the child's personality and character. Children are in dire need of guidance and leadership. They must be taught to shoulder responsibility, to understand the importance of education and develop the self-discipline which is a necessary ingredient in the formula of life with its pitfalls and dangers.

"To eliminate forever the cruel, unjust fate of the underprivileged children, we must awaken the public to the urgent needs of the younger generation.

"We must interest and gain the help of organizations far and wide with the promotion of a square deal for underprivileged children. When we have that, we will have splendid, educated citizens, mold fine character and produce fewer criminals. The result will be a happier and industrious people that will always keep our America the greatest country in the world."

QUOTES FROM DR. JACOB BOLOTIN

Kiwanis is that want for service that grows in the inner recess of a man's heart and soul, peaking the highest level of character and binding him forever to the Golden Rule.

Kiwanis is that ideal which is so closely interwoven with good citizenship that I cannot conceive how an American can be one without being the other.

Kiwanis is that happy spirit that makes the underprivileged forget their handicap and the pessimist forget his troubles.

Kiwanis takes all that is positive and negative in a man's nature, puts the positive to work and the negative to shame.

When you meet a Kiwanian, you meet a live wire charged 100% with Kiwanis activity, building a mountain of personal service, and extending the ideals of Kiwanis to the distant parts of the earth.

To me, Kiwanis is the missing link which has been supplied to a chain which has linked me up with the rest of the progressive world. I can no longer be unhappy, for Kiwanis is always with me, and there will never be a day when Kiwanis and Boy Scouts will not enjoin me to do a good turn.

If Kiwanis has done all this, meant all this, and made all this possible for me, I can but ask my God and my country to make me a 100% Kiwanian in giving me a chance to serve others even as I have been served.

I am a very happy man and I live in a different world from most sighted people. I love the birds and the flowers and the woods and parks of nature. I can go for an auto ride or to a show, or any place of amusement and find a great deal of entertainment in going to these places. Often, I make my friends see for me, in many cases without their knowledge.

POETRY

by Jacob Bolotin

I love to compose poetry. While I know nothing of poetry, and my rhymes are imperfect, their thought is worth considering, and I would like to leave a few of my "Homemade" poems with you.

MY MOTTO

When you meet a man who's blind,
Don't feel sorry but try to find;
Not a poorhouse where he can shirk,
But a job he wants to work.

I DO THE BEST I CAN

I don't always find things easy,
And many times I foil,
When the wind's too strong one way,
I simply change my soil.

When sorrow strikes or bad luck hits
I do the best I can
And when I win the battle
I'm a stronger, better man.

ABOUT KIWANIS

My luck is most peculiar
As it follows me each day,
Sometimes it brings me sadness
And sometimes it brings me play.

But, somehow, I never thought to quit
In the face of luck's bad trend,
But meet each obstacle with grit
And make of it my friend.

And now that I'm a Kiwanian
And my duty is "to build,"
I want no well-filled pocketbook
Or soil already tilled.

I want to roll my sleeves up high
And get into the game,
If I'm to be worth anything
I'll work my way to fame.

Let's be to each other a Kiwanian big brother,
To our motto most faithful and true.
Let's do some kind deed for the fellow in need
And give him a life to pull through.

Let's rent him a home in the world of Kiwanis,
He can play by helping us build,
And won't we be proud when he laughs with a joy
With which his heart is filled.

Kiwanis says, "We build"
Kiwanians will never shirk.
The blind man wants to help,
But the public won't let him work.

It's up to you, Kiwanians,
Don't sympathize or sob.
Just put your shoulder to the wheel
And find the blind a job.

More than money, more than fame,
Will be to me the day,
When every sightless, jobless man,
Will draw his first week's pay.

A SMILE

A smile is a gift which one can give,
With very little cost;
Yet giving is an opportunity
Many folks have lost.

To receive it is a blessing
Which some have seldom had,
To reject it means a burden
Which keeps some poor heart sad.

So get out, boys, and give a smile
As only good-fellows can,
And you will help make life worthwhile,
For your fellow man.

CHAIN OF FRIENDSHIP

You may all have your golf and your football,
You may all have good shows that you see;
But there is a game, called the "Chain of Friendship,"
That's good enough sport for me.

And believe me, boys, I love to play it;
And I'm going to show you just how I play;
It's a game you can't spoil by snow or by rain,
It's a game played any old day.

It's played by building great chains from great links;
And each link must be strong and true.
For when the chain is done, the game is won,
And each link has a service to do.

I am playing "The Chain of Friendship,"
Each link in the chain is my friend;
And whenever I meet a Kiwanian,
He helps me to build and to friend.

May I feel that you'll become builders
Each one of a link of my chain,
If I may, I'm happy today,
And that's playing the game.

ABOUT THE AUTHOR

Rosalind Perlman in 1994

Rosalind Perlman was born in Chicago in 1911. She was educated at Washington University in St. Louis, Missouri, and later at St. Louis Teachers College.

She met her husband, Alfred, when she returned to Chicago after completing her education, and they were married in 1938. While Alfred was serving in Army quartermaster corps during World War II, Rosalind wrote and produced a weekly radio series for the Chicago Tribune station, WGN, and taught script writing. After Alfred returned from serving overseas, the couple moved to Santa Maria, California in 1952, where Alfred taught high school.

In Santa Maria, Rosalind taught speech and drama at Hancock College for the Pacific Conservatory for the Performing Arts, where she frequently acted as well as starred in productions. She also wrote a regular column for the Santa Maria Times. Both she and Alfred were very involved in their community.

The completion and publication of *The Blind Doctor: The Jacob Bolotin Story* was the dream they worked on together until Alfred's death in 2001 at the age of 92. Rosalind continued to work on the manuscript and, with her bequest to the Santa Barbara Foundation, finally made sure that Jacob's story would be told. And by setting up the annual Dr. Jacob Bolotin Award to be given out by the National Federation of the Blind, she carried on his legacy by honoring other exceptional individuals who happen to be blind. Rosalind died in 2004 at the age of 93.

SANTA BARBARA FOUNDATION

For **good**. For **ever.**[SM]

The Santa Barbara Foundation was established in 1928 to enrich the lives of the people of Santa Barbara County through philanthropy. Major Max Fleischmann, heir to the Fleischmann Yeast/Gin fortune, originally established the Foundation with $250,000 of Standard Brands stock to fund free open-air band concerts for the people of Santa Barbara. By the mid-1930s, Major Fleischmann had removed all restrictions upon his gifts to the Foundation and encouraged its growth as a general charitable organization.

Over the years, the Santa Barbara Foundation has grown through subsequent contribution from thousands of local donors and funds hundreds of area nonprofits to enhance the quality of life for everyone in Santa Barbara County. In 1980, the Santa Barbara News-Press wrote, "It is not too much to say that just about every citizen of this area has been touched by the Foundation's giving."

As a community foundation, the Santa Barbara Foundation is a resource for philanthropy, working with individual donors and local, regional, and national grantmakers. It works to make the important connection between an individual's personal passions and their charitable dreams.

Rosalind Perlman first approached the Foundation in 2004. She wanted to honor the accomplishments of her husband's uncle, Dr. Jacob Bolotin, and to publish a book about his life. The Foundation helped Rosalind establish the Alfred and Rosalind Perlman Fund and undertook the publication of her book, *The Blind Doctor*, and the creation of the Dr. Jacob Bolotin Award for the Blind. This award will be given out annually by the National Federation of the Blind to blind people or organizations that have made a significant impact within the blind community.

For more information about the Santa Barbara Foundation visit www.sbfoundation.org.

NFB
National Federation of the Blind

With over fifty thousand members, the National Federation of the Blind is the largest and most influential membership organization of blind people in the United States. The organization has affiliates in all fifty states, the District of Columbia, and Puerto Rico, as well as over seven hundred local chapters. The NFB was founded in 1940 to serve as a vehicle for collective action and self-expression by the blind, and today its members work through its local chapters, state affiliates, and the annual national convention to achieve democratically adopted policies and goals. For this reason, it is known as the "Voice of the Nation's Blind."

The National Federation of the Blind is guided by the philosophy that the real problem of blindness is not the loss of eyesight, but the misunderstanding and lack of information that exist. If a blind person is given proper training and opportunity, blindness can be reduced to the level of a physical nuisance. The goal of the National Federation of the Blind is the complete integration of the blind into society on the basis of equality.

The NFB improves blind people's lives through advocacy, education, research, technology, and programs encouraging independence and self-confidence. Some of the organization's many achievements include the creation and maintenance of the world's largest audio newspaper service for the blind, the development (with inventor Ray Kurzweil) of the first handheld device capable of converting text on a printed page into synthesized speech, and groundbreaking programs designed to encourage the participation of blind youth in science, technology, engineering, and mathematics.

National Federation of the Blind will be giving out the annual Dr. Jacob Bolotin Award to blind people or organizations that have made a significant impact within the blind community beginning in 2008.

For more information or to support the National Federation of the Blind, visit www.nfb.org.

HOW TO ORDER

The Blind Doctor
The Jacob Bolotin Story

By Rosalind Perlman

can be ordered directly from Blue Point Books

**VISA®/MASTERCARD® ORDERS call toll free:
1-800-858-1058**

or order on our website at
www.bluepointbooks.com

Each book is **$19.95** plus $3.00 shipping and handling

A Large Type edition also available. The cost is $24.95
plus $3.00 shipping and handling

For information about purchasing our books in quantity
for your organization or company, please contact:

Blue Point Books

P.O. Box 91347, Santa Barbara, CA 93190-1347
800-858-1058
fax: 805-687-0282 • e-mail: bpbooks@west.net

The proceeds from the sales of *The Blind Doctor* go the Alfred and Rosalind Perlman Trust at the Santa Barbara Foundation. This Trust funds an annual award, the Dr. Jacob Bolotin Award, which is given to the blind people or organizations that have made a significant impact within the blind community. The first Award will be given out in 2008 by the National Federation of the Blind. For more information, visit www.sbfoundation.org